G000138897

Condition Monitoring
of Electrical Machines

ELECTRONIC & ELECTRICAL ENGINEERING RESEARCH STUDIES

ELECTRICAL MACHINES SERIES

Series Editor: **Dr Peter J. Tavner**
Laurence, Scott and Electromotors Ltd., England

1. Condition Monitoring of Electrical Machines
   Peter J. Tavner and James Penman

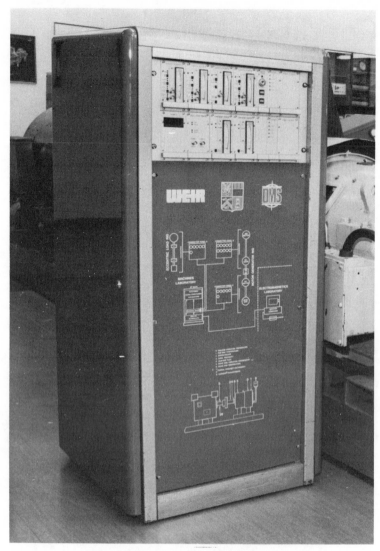

A fully automated monitoring system
(Courtesy of Weir Pumps Ltd. and D.M.S. Ltd.)

Condition Monitoring of Electrical Machines

Peter J. Tavner
Chief Electrical Engineer
Laurence, Scott and Electromotors Ltd.
Norwich, UK

and

James Penman
Reader in Electrical Engineering
University of Aberdeen, UK

RESEARCH STUDIES PRESS LTD.
Letchworth, Hertfordshire, England

JOHN WILEY & SONS INC.
New York · Chichester · Toronto · Brisbane · Singapore

RESEARCH STUDIES PRESS LTD.
58B Station Road, Letchworth, Herts. SG6 3BE, England

Copyright © 1987, by Research Studies Press Ltd.

Marketing and Distribution:

Australia, New Zealand, South-east Asia:
Jacaranda-Wiley Ltd., Jacaranda Press
JOHN WILEY & SONS INC.
GPO Box 859, Brisbane, Queensland 4001, Australia

Canada:
JOHN WILEY & SONS CANADA LIMITED
22 Worcester Road, Rexdale, Ontario, Canada

Europe, Africa:
JOHN WILEY & SONS LIMITED
Baffins Lane, Chichester, West Sussex, England

North and South America and the rest of the world:
JOHN WILEY & SONS INC.
605 Third Avenue, New York, NY 10158, USA

Library of Congress Cataloging in Publication Data

Tavner, Peter J., 1946–
  Condition monitoring of electrical machines.
  (Electronic & electrical engineering research
studies. Electrical machines series; 1)
  Bibliography: p.
  Includes indexes.
  1. Electric machinery—Monitoring. I. Penman,
James. II. Title. III. Series.
TK2313.T38   1987   621.31'042   87-20691

ISBN 0 86380 061 0
ISBN 0 471 91753 2 (Wiley)

British Library Cataloguing in Publication Data

Tavner, Peter J.
  Condition monitoring of electrical
  machines.
  1. Machinery——Testing
  I. Title   II. Penman, James
  621.8'16   TJ153

ISBN 0 86380 061 0
ISBN 0 471 91753 2 (Wiley)

  ISBN 0 86380 061 0 (Research Studies Press Ltd.)
  ISBN 0 471 91753 2 (John Wiley & Sons Inc.)

Printed in Great Britain by SRP Ltd., Exeter

To Elizabeth and Eileen

Preface

Condition monitoring of engineering plant has increased in importance as more and more engineering processes are automated and the manpower needed to operate and supervise plant is reduced. But electrical machinery has traditionally been thought of as reliable and requiring very little attention, except at infrequent intervals when the plant is shut down for inspection. Rotating electrical machines, however, are at the core of most engineering processes and as machines are designed to tighter margins there is a growing need, for reliability's sake, to monitor their behaviour and performance on-line.

This book is intended to be a guide to the techniques which are available. Condition monitoring of electrical machines as a whole covers a very wide field including rotating machines and transformers and could include the many off-line inspection techniques. To restrict the field we have confined ourselves to rotating machines only and to techniques which can be applied when those machines are in operation.

We have had experience in devising and applying monitoring techniques. On the one hand in the university where many new ideas have been developed and refined. On the other in the supply and manufacturing industries where techniques have been applied and operational experience has shown which are the most serviceable. We hope that we give you a comprehensive survey of the techniques available and that we have given sufficient references for the reader to follow up those methods which may be of particular value to him.

There are no golden rules as to which techniques are best and the user must tailor them to suit the particular plant he needs to monitor. However, it is certain that as the condition monitoring of electrical machinery develops there will be an increasing emphasis upon the presentation of information from monitoring devices and aiding decision-making based upon that information. This will inevitably involve the processing of monitoring information in computers and we hope that our readers will be able to use what they learn here to progress that development.

A book such as this, which surveys a wide range of developments, could not be written without the assistance of many colleagues and friends. In particular Dr. Tavner would like to thank the Scientific Services Department at South Eastern Region CEGB for allowing him to start work upon the book and the Directors of Laurence Scott and Electromotors Ltd. for allowing him to finish it.

Dr. Penman would also like to thank Professor J.R. Smith for his encouragement, and express his gratitude to Shell U.K. Exploration and Production for several fruitful discussions when they provided the technical details referred to in Chapter 8. Particular thanks are due to Mr. D. Hartley and Mr. K. Thomson, in this respect.

The book was carefully typed at Gravesend by Mrs A. Robertson and Miss K. Street, and at Aberdeen by Miss A. Shipley. Thanks are also due to Miss A.M. Hayden, Mrs F. Smith, and Mr. S. Cutts for the careful production of the graphical material that appears in the book.

Photographs and diagrams have been provided by a number of different organisations and we would like to thank Brüel & Kjær, Convex Designs Ltd., GEC Ltd., the Central Electricity Generating Board, Hewlett Packard Ltd., the Institution of Electrical Engineers, the Institution of Electrical and Electronic Engineers, NEI Electronics Ltd., Gabriel Microwave Systems Ltd., Shell UK Expro, Laurence, Scott and Electromotors Ltd., Smith Industries Ltd., NEI Parsons Ltd., and Weir Pumps Ltd.

Contents

CHAPTER EIGHT   THE APPLICATION OF MONITORING —
                  CASE STUDIES

CHAPTER 1

The Case for Monitoring

1.1 INTRODUCTION

Rotating electrical machines permeate all areas of modern life at both the domestic and industrial level. The average home will contain approximately 20 to 30 electrical motors in clocks, domestic appliances, toys, and heating systems. Such motors will generally be rated in the 0 to 1 kW range.

We also depend, directly and indirectly, upon machines of greater rating and relative complexity in order to support our general standard of living. The electricity we use so freely is generated in machines whose rating can exceed 1 000 MW, and which have evolved to a state of great sophistication. A substantial proportion of the food we buy is kept fresh by chilling, or air conditioning, using systems centred on electrical machinery. Many of the domestic products we use are made directly from, or are packaged in, by-products of the petro-chemicals industry. Process industries of this kind rely heavily on electrical machinery to transport and control the feed stocks and reactions required to produce the plastics and fibres we take so much for granted.

The steel used to make our car will have been rolled using large electrical machines, and at an earlier stage still the furnaces will have been charged using yet more electrical machines. Without them our society would quickly cease to function.

We begin to appreciate the overall picture now. Electrical machines come in many sizes. They fulfil their function either largely independent of other items of plant, or they can be part of a highly complex process in which all elements must function smoothly so that production can be maintained. It is the usage of electrical machinery in the latter role that has risen dramatically with the passage of time, and there is no reason to suspect that this trend will do anything other than accelerate in the coming decades.

Historically, however, the idea that the function of an individual electrical machine was easily separable from the rest of the electrical or mechanical system was the prevalent one. Also, it must be remembered that in general terms the reliability

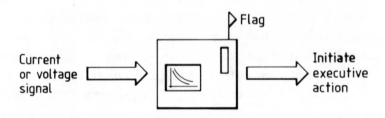

Figure 1.1 : The basic function of the protective relay

of electrical machines is very high. It is against this background that the basic principles of protective relaying evolved. Protection is designed to intercept faults as they occur and to initiate action that ensures that the minimum of further damage occurs before failure. In its basic form the protective relay has the function outlined in Figure 1.1.

The signal provided by the transducer will be in the form of a current or voltage, and will be interpreted by the relay as an acceptable, or unacceptable, level according to a pre-set value worked out by the relay designer or the maintenance staff. If the pre-set value is exceeded then the relay will initiate further electromechanical action that will often result in disconnection of the electrical machine, and it will flag the fact that a fault, or even failure, has been identified. This is, of course, a simplistic view of the protective relay. Many

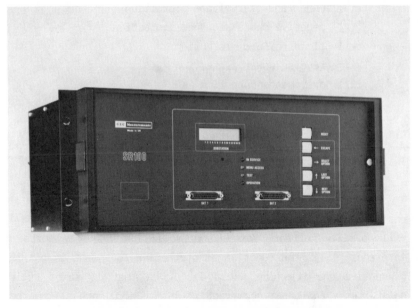

Figure 1.2 : A typical modern relay
(Courtesy of GEC Ltd.)

available today have a wide range of functions, and are indeed programmable to allow more sophisticated criteria for initiating interrupt procedures to be applied. For example it is desirable to block the restart of a motor until it has cooled to an acceptable degree. Figure 1.2 shows a typical modern programmable relay for fulfilling such a function.

From what has been said above it is apparent that protective relaying can be regarded as a form of monitoring, and indeed it is widely used with great success. Virtually all electrical machine protection systems embody some form of electro-mechanical devices, and on typical machines they are used in some or all of the following schemes:

   (i)   earth fault protection
  (ii)   overcurrent protection
 (iii)   differential current protection
  (iv)   under and overvoltage protection
   (v)   negative phase sequence protection
  (vi)   field failure protection
 (vii)   reverse power protection
(viii)   overspeed protection
  (ix)   excessive vibration protection
   (x)   thermal overload protection.

This list is representative rather than complete.

It is important to stress the fact that protection is basically designed to act only once a fault has occurred, and it will normally initiate some executive action. In the words of Reference [1.1] 'the function of protective equipment is not the preventive one its name would imply, in that it takes action only after a fault has occurred; it is the ambulance at the foot of the cliff rather than the fence at the top'.

The executive action may very well be the disconnection of the piece of machinery from the supply. Such action is acceptable if the item of plant is readily dissociated from the process it is involved with, or if it exists substantially in isolation. If, however, the piece of plant is vital to the operation of a process then an unscheduled shutdown of the complete process may occur. The losses involved may then be significantly greater than those resulting simply due to loss of output during a scheduled shutdown. It must also be borne in mind that the capital cost of an individual machine is more often than not small compared with the capital costs involved in a plant shutdown. Maintenance is most effective when it is planned to service many items in the course of a single outage. In summary monitoring is not necessarily aimed solely at the individual machine, but at the wider health of the process of which it is part.

1.2 THE NEED FOR MONITORING

The notion of the scheduled shutdown introduces one logically to the case that can be made on behalf of monitoring. By condition monitoring we mean the continuous evaluation of the health of plant and equipment throughout its serviceable life. Condition monitoring and protection are obviously closely re-lated functions. The approach to the implementation of each is, however, quite different. Also the advantages that accrue due to monitoring are entirely different to those to be expected from protection.

This is principally because monitoring should be designed so as to pre-empt faults, whereas protection is essentially retro-active. Condition monitoring can, in many cases, be extended to provide primary protection, but its real function must always be to attempt to recognise the development of faults at an early stage. Such advanced warning is obviously desirable since it allows maintenance staff greater freedom to schedule outages in the most convenient manner, resulting in lower down time and lower capitalised losses.

We have said above that advanced warnings of mal-functions, as provided by monitoring, are obviously desirable. Are they? We must justify this because the implementation of a monitoring system can involve the operator in considerable expense. There are other questions to be answered too. For example, once one has chosen to embark upon a programme of monitoring what form should it take? Should the monitoring be intermittent, or regular at fixed time intervals, or should it be continuous? If one employs a fixed time interval maintenance programme then is it necessary to monitor at all? Monitoring can generate large quantities of data; how can this information be best used to minimise future expenditure? Finally, and perhaps most importantly, how much needs to be spent on monitoring in order to make it truly effective? Very few of these questions have simple answers but we can get some indications by considering the magnitude of the maintenance and replacement burden that industry is continually facing, and the implications for the costs of various maintenance strategies. We will consider three different courses of action:

   (i)   breakdown maintenance;
  (ii)   fixed time interval maintenance;
 (iii)   maintenance on the basis of condition.

Plan (i) demands no more than a 'run it until it breaks then replace it' strategy, whilst method (ii) may or may not involve a limited degree of monitoring. The final scenario requires a definite commitment to monitoring.

The scale of the problem can be estimated by examining some of the figures provided by the 'Neale Report' [1.2], published in 1979. Table 1.1 shows the annual investment per employee in plant and machinery. We have modified these values in order to reflect more realistically today's costs and have selected those industries which would have a high proportion of expenditure in electrical machinery and ancillary plant.

TABLE 1.1   EXPENDITURE ON PLANT PER EMPLOYEE
OF SELECTED INDUSTRIES
ADAPTED FROM REFERENCE [1.2]

Industry	Annual investment/employee in plant and machinery in £
Electrical Engineering	400
Electricial Supply	8 000
Chemical Industry	2 400
Textiles	600
Instrumentation Production	400
Oil refining	14 000
Iron and Steel	1 800
North Sea Oil and Gas	160 000
Water Supply	800

The same report shows that the average annual expenditure on maintenance was 80% of the amount annually invested in plant and machinery. The figures for some selected industries and industrial groupings are shown in Table 1.2, which shows the annual maintenance expenditure as a percentage of the annual plant investment expenditure. This is obviously a high figure in real terms and anything that helps to reduce it must be welcome. The Hewlett-Packard Journal [1.3] quotes the staggering figure of $200 billion as the annual maintenance bill for U.S. business, and a growth rate of 12%. Now only a fraction of this sum will be spent on maintaining electrical machinery, but even if it amounts to only points of percent. of the total it is still an enormous amount of money

Clearly there are great incentives to maintain plant more efficiently, particularly when it is estimated that approximately 70% of the maintenance work carried out by companies that use no planning at all may be classified as emergency work. It is apparent that careful thought must be given to the most appropriate form of maintenance planning. For example breakdown maintenance can only be effective when there is a substantial amount of redundant capacity, and a single breakdown does not cause the failure of a complete system. The question to be answered in such circumstances is, 'why is there a significant redundancy'? And should it be allowed to continue?

Many sectors of industry, and particularly electricity supply, have adopted maintenance planning based on replacement and overhaul at fixed time intervals. Such scheduling is usually planned on the basis of a limited amount of condition monitoring, and the monitoring is typically not done on a continuous basis. There are many estimates of the savings that accrue by adopting such an approach, and an average figure of 60% of the total maintenance burden may be considered reasonable. This is obviously good news, but it must be treated cautiously because such a maintenance policy makes heavy demands upon scarce, skilled manpower. Also, it is estimated that only 10% of components replaced during fixed interval maintenance outages actually needs to be replaced at that time. The obvious implication is that 90% of what is replaced need not be.

TABLE 1.2   ANNUAL MAINTENANCE EXPENDITURE AS A PERCENTAGE OF ANNUAL CAPITAL INVESTMENT IN PLANT, FOR SELECTED INDUSTRIES
ADAPTED FROM REFERENCE [1.2]

Industry	$\dfrac{\text{Maintenance Expenditure}}{\text{Plant Expenditure}}$
Coal Products	26%
Iron and Steel	42%
Marine Engineering	50%
Chemical Industries	78%
Electrical Machinery	80%
Electricity Supply	80%
Gas Supply	80%
Water Supply	80%
Textiles	82%
Mechanical Engineering	100%
Instrumentation Production	150%
Printing	160%

Such considerations, and the realisation that modern electrical machines and the processes they operate in are growing in complexity, leads one to the conclusion that continuous condition monitoring of certain critical items of plant can lead to significant benefits. These benefits accrue as a result of greater plant efficiency, reduced capitalised losses due to breakdown, and reduced replacement costs. The plant operator can also be continually updated with information on the performance of his machinery. This will help him to improve the day to day operational availability and efficiency of the plant. Condition monitoring should give information relevant to both the operational and maintenance functions as shown in Figure 1.3. There is also the important additional consideration that better maintenance gives better safety. In the longer term, condition monitoring also allows the operator to build up a data base which can be used for trend analysis, so that further improvements can be made in the scheduling of maintenance. Such information should also be used advantageously by the manufacturers and designers of plant in order to further improve product reliability. This step effectively 'closes the loop' as illustrated in Figure 1.3.

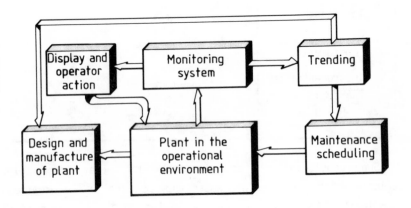

Figure 1.3 : The place of condition monitoring

In view of the above, how much needs to be spent on monitoring? This depends on the value of the process in which the machine works, and estimates vary, but they are never less than 1% of the capital value of the plant being monitored. A more typical, and probably more realistic, figure would be 5% for the general run of industrial processes, whilst special requirements for high value processes, such as those found in the offshore oil and gas industry, may push a realistic figure to greater than 10%.

1.3 WHAT, AND WHEN TO MONITOR

Now that we have examined some of the advantages to be gained from a commitment to condition monitoring we can briefly address the questions, what should we monitor, and when? The question, what to monitor, has two implications; what machines and what parameters. The first part is more easily answered. In view of the capital costs involved in providing monitoring, whether it takes the form of a permanent installation with its own local intelligence, or a hand-held device used periodically by a skilled operator, it is unlikely that electrical machines with ratings less than 20 kW would benefit. There are, of course, exceptions to this where a smaller machine has a vital function in the performance of a larger system. It will always pay dividends to carefully consider the implications of losing the output of an individual piece of machinery, in the context of a complete system.

Larger electrical drives that support generating plant will benefit from monitoring, although perhaps not continuous monitoring, if a high margin of spare capacity exists. One could include induced and forced-draught boiler fan drives, boiler water feed pump drives, and cooling water pump drives in power stations, in this category. It must always be borne in mind, however, that successful monitoring can allow a big reduction in the requirement for on-site spare capacity.

Machines which have a high penalty in lost output costs need to be monitored continually. Turbogenerators naturally fall into this category since lost output can exceed £0.5M/day for a large, high merit machine.

The conclusion is that there are machines to which monitoring is readily applicable, but there are other circumstances where careful assessment is needed before deciding. One must always be mindful of the scale of the maintenance burden however and not be driven to false economies on the basis that 'nothing has gone wrong so far'. On the other hand one must bear in mind the complexities of the monitoring system itself and its own maintenance burden. Nothing can be worse than to invest in complex monitoring equipment which because of poor design or maintenance gives rise to large numbers of false alarms, which lead to the equipment being eventually ignored.

The parameters to be monitored are essentially those that will provide the operator and maintainer with sufficient details to make informed decisions on operation and maintenance scheduling, but which ensure security of plant operation. Automatic, on-line, monitoring has only recently begun to make an impact in the area of electrical machines. Traditionally quantities, such as line currents and voltages, core temperatures, bearing vibration levels, have been measured and will continue to be used. Other quantities, involving the sensing of pyrolysed products in cooling gases and oils, have recently been introduced, as have techniques for measuring contamination levels in bearing lubricants. Other specialist methods, involving the accurate measurement of rotational speed, or the sensing of leakage fluxes, are being developed in order to monitor a variety of fault conditions.

As the ready availability of sophisticated electronic and microprocessor-based systems is translated into monitoring hardware,then the more variables it is possible to consider, and the more comprehensive the monitoring can be. This trend will be further accelerated as the costs of computing power fall still further, and the complexity of microprocessors increases. Such developments are essential both because of the complexity of the plant being monitored and the complexity of the monitoring signals themselves.

It is tempting to think that,with such a degree of monitoring power becoming available, the protective and monitoring functions could be merged. This will undoubtedly eventually happen, but until a considerable degree of operational experience is built up these functions must remain separate.

The question when to monitor, is more easily answered. One should monitor when it is cost-effective to do so, or when there are over-riding safety considerations to be observed. The assessment of cost-effectiveness can be a relatively complex matter, but in general terms monitoring is worthwhile when the net annual savings are increased by its use. The net annual saving is the difference between the gross annual saving and the annual costs. The costs of monitoring include the initial investigation, purchase, and installation charges, the staff training costs, and the costs associated with the data acquisition. This expenditure can be written off over the life time of the monitoring system and set against the savings accrued. We have already considered these savings in some detail, earlier in this Chapter,and it is sufficient to say that it is not uncommon for the capital costs of a wisely chosen monitoring system to be retrieved in the first year of its operational life.

14

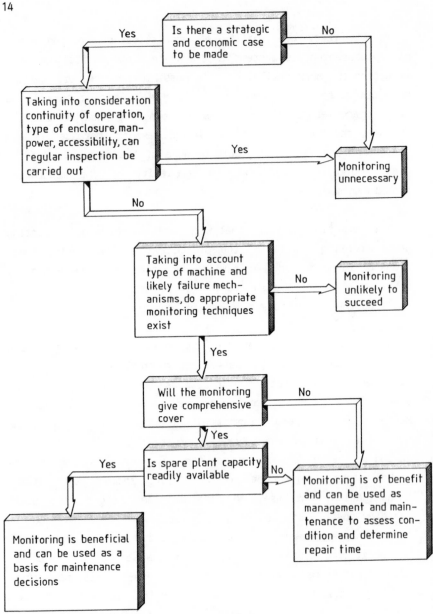

Figure 1.4 : How to decide whether monitoring is worth
doing, or not

Some of the questions asked here, and the routes towards the appropriate answer, are illustrated in the form of a decision tree, in Figure 1.4.

1.4 SCOPE OF THE TEXT

Some time ago the authors recognised the need to draw together into a single source an account of the techniques available to any one wishing to involve themselves in the monitoring of electrical machines. It is an area of technology that is extremely wide-ranging, requiring a knowledge of: the performance of electrical machines, the design of microprocessor-based instrumentation, signal processing, material and chemical analysis, and vibration analysis. Obviously in a book of this length it is neither possible nor indeed desirable to enter into a detailed study of any one of these areas. We have instead set ourselves the objective of covering the complete monitoring field, as it relates to electrical machinery, in a manner that will be useful to anyone wishing to become familiar with the subject for the first time, and will assist people actively engaged in condition monitoring to gain a perspective of new developments.

The text is readily divisible into three distinct sections. The first is essentially 'a description of the patient, the things that can go wrong with him, and a general guide to the diagnosis'. It is contained in Chapters 2 and 3 and provides a broad guide to electrical machine construction, and the general considerations applicable to monitoring systems.

The second section, comprising Chapters 4, 5, 6 and 7, gives a relatively detailed account of the more important monitoring techniques. These techniques are separated into, electrical, chemical, mechanical and thermal methods, although there will obviously be areas of overlap between each of them. As far as possible we have subdivided the techniques within each chapter into the types and parts of machines on which they are used. In these sections we describe current practice and discuss some of the new developments now being introduced. We treat instrumentation largely at the functional level only, and assume a certain basic knowledge of the techniques of spectral analysis of signals.

The third section, in Chapter 8, takes the form of case studies to root the previous work firmly in practice. The cases have been chosen to be representative of the range of conditions normally encountered in monitoring. They are the monitoring of turbogenerators, large drives in the oil industry, and high integrity machines operating in a power station.

We have also tried to be mindful of the fact that, when discussing developments in a relatively new subject area, a comprehensive bibliography is of the utmost importance. This is provided at the end of the book. It is inevitable that there will be omissions but hopefully it will provide the interested reader with a useful source of additional material.

CHAPTER 2

The Construction and Operation of Electrical Machines and the Way they Fail in Service

2.1 INTRODUCTION

Rotating electrical machines convert electrical to mechanical energy, or vice versa, and they achieve this by magnetically coupling electrical circuits across an air gap that permits rotational freedom of one of these circuits. Mechanical energy is transmitted into, or out of, the machine via a drive train that is mechanically connected to one of the electric circuits. The construction of all electrical machines and their operational weaknesses are dominated by these principles.

The magnetic and electric circuits require materials of high permeability and low resistivity respectively. Now metals with good magnetic and electrical properties do not necessarily have high mechanical strength. Indeed the atomic structure of a good conductor is such that it will naturally have a low yield strength and high ductility. Yet the magnetic and electric circuits of the machine must bear the mechanical loads imposed upon them by the transfer of energy across the airgap. Furthermore, the magnetic and electrical circuits must be separated by insulating materials, such as papers and plastics, which have even more feeble mechanical properties. Table 2.1 sets out the elastic moduli and tensile strength of materials used in electrical machines and highlights the relative weakness of magnetic steel, conductor and insulating materials. So right from the outset there is 'a conflict between the electrical and mechanical requirements of the various parts of an electrical machine, which the designer must attempt to resolve.

TABLE 2.1   MECHANICAL PROPERTIES OF MATERIALS USED IN
ELECTRICAL MACHINES

Material	Elastic Modulus GN/m^2	Tensile Strength MN/m^2
Structural steel	210	600-1000
Electrical steel	220	450
Copper	120	210
Aluminium	70	310
Epoxy-mica paper	60	275
Shellac-mica paper	30	125
Moulded organic and inorganic insulation	5	48
Phenol-formaldehyde resins	3	35

Taken from Reference [2.1]

There is a further complication, however. The transfer of energy inevitably involves the dissipation of heat, by ohmic losses in the electric circuit, and by eddy current and hysteresis losses in the magnetic circuit. The performance of the insulating materials which keep these circuits apart is highly dependent upon temperature, and deteriorates rapidly at high temperatures. The following Table 2.2, taken from the British Standard on insulating materials, shows the relatively low temperatures at which they are permitted to operate.

TABLE 2.2   TEMPERATURE CAPABILITIES OF
INSULATING MATERIALS

Class	Material	Temperature Limit to give an acceptable life under usual industrial conditions of service
Y	Materials or combinations of materials such as cotton, silk and paper without impregnation.	90°C
A	Materials such as cotton, silk and paper when suitably impregnated or coated or immersed in a dielectric liquid such as oil.	105°C
E	Material such as synthetic-resin impregnated and enamelled wire not containing fibrous materials such as cotton, silk or paper.	120°C
B	Materials or combinations of materials such as mica, glass fibre, asbestos etc., with suitable bonding, impregnating or coating substances.	130°C
F	Materials or combinations of materials such as mica, glass, asbestos etc. with suitable bonding, impregnating or coating substances.	155°C
H	Materials such as silicone elastomer and combinations of materials such as mica, glass fibre, asbestos, etc. with suitable bonding, impregnating or coating substances such as appropriate silicone resins.	180°C
C	Materials or combinations of materials such as mica, porcelain, glass, quartz and asbestos, with or without an organic binder.	180°C

Uncertainties about the temperature within a machine mean that the designer is forced to restrict the maximum measurable operating temperature to an even lower value than that given in Table 2.2, for the appropriate insulation. It is clear that the heat dissipated within a machine must be removed effectively if design limits are to be met. For example, in a 660 MW turbogenerator with losses of the order of 10 MW, if no cooling were present the average temperature of the generator body would exceed any of the maximum permitted insulation temperatures within 12 sec. The problem is exacerbated because the losses are not evenly distributed and in practice at some locations the temperature will rise even faster than this and so cooling considerations become a vital part of machine design.

Clearly the health of an electrical machine is ultimately related to the sorts of materials of which it is made, with the mechanical and electrical stresses they are under, and with the temperatures they can attain during service.

In Chapter 1 we explained how electrical machines are protected by relays which, in general, sense any serious disruption of the current flowing in the winding and operate to trip or disconnect the machine. Some warning of a machine failure can be obtained simply by making the protective relays especially sensitive and providing an alarm indication before tripping occurs. When fault currents are flowing the machine has already failed as an electrical device. But an electrical or mechanical fault is always preceded by deterioration of one of the mechanical, electrical, magnetic, insulation or cooling components of the machine. This is so, regardless of the type of electrical machine. If that deterioration takes a significant period of time and can be detected by measurement then that detection may be a valuable means of monitoring the machine before failure. The heart of condition monitoring is to derive methods to measure, as directly as possible, parameters which indicate that deterioration and provide sufficient warning of impending failure in order that the machine may be taken off for repair or may be tripped before serious damage occurs.

2.2 THE CONSTRUCTION OF ELECTRICAL MACHINES

The basic constructional features of the electrical machine are shown in Figure 2.1.

The rotor, which usually has a relatively high inertia, is supported on two bearings which may be mounted on separate pedestals or incorporated into the enclosure of the machine. Rolling element bearings are used on smaller size machines where shaft peripheral velocities are low, and sleeve bearings are used for larger machines. Vertically-mounted machines will incorporate

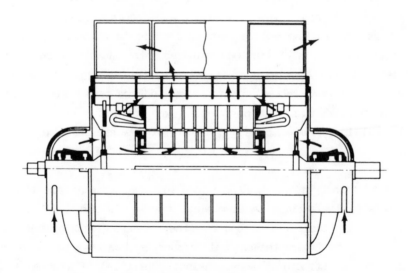

Figure 2.1 : Basic constructional features of an
electrical machine
(Courtesy of Laurence, Scott & Electromotors Ltd.)

a thrust bearing usually at the low end of the enclosure. This may be a relatively modest bearing for a small vertically mounted pump motor but can be a large bearing with Mitchell thrust pads for a hydro-type generator where the rotor may weigh 100 tonnes or more. The design of the rotor will depend on the particular type of machine. Induction and d.c. motors have laminated rotors where the laminations are clamped together and shrunk onto the steel shaft. Turbine-type generators have large, solid, forged-steel rotors which are long and thin, while hydro-type generators have large, short, fat rotors with laminated pole shoes bolted onto a fabricated spider. Where air or gas cooling is necessary an axial, or radial, fan may be fitted at either or both ends of the rotor shaft. However, smaller machines rely solely on air circulation as a result of the windage of the rotor itself, which is usually slotted to accept the rotor windings.

The rotor windings of generators are constructed of hard-drawn copper and are insulated with rigid epoxy or formaldehyde resin, impregnated into a woven material. On squirrel cage induction motors the winding may consist of lightly insulated copper bars driven into the slots in the laminated rotor or of aluminium bars cast directly into the rotor. The rotor windings of a d.c. machine or wound rotor induction motor will be rather similar to a conventional a.c. stator winding which is described later. Typical induction motor and generator rotors are shown in Figure 2.2.

The stators of all a.c. machines are constructed from lightly insulated laminations of electrical steel. As Table 2.1 shows, electrical steels are strong but the silicon, incorporated into the alloy to impart the magnetic properties, weakens the material compared to structural steel, making it brittle. Furthermore if the laminated structure is to have the cohesion necessary to transmit the load torque, and have low levels of vibration when carrying the magnetic flux, it must be firmly clamped between cast

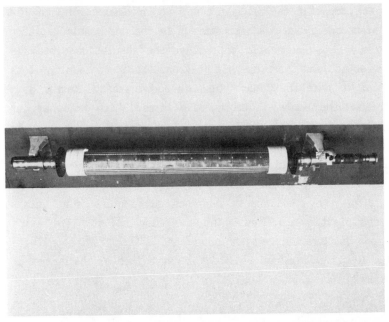

Figure 2.2 : Typical induction motor and generator rotors
(Courtesy of Laurence, Scott & Electromotors Ltd. and
NEI Parsons Ltd.)

or fabricated end-plates which are secured to a cylindrical frame into which the core is keyed. The core is constructed within the frame and compressed before the clamping plates are applied. On larger machines the clamping plates are tightened by large bolts, see Figure 2.3, but on smaller machines interlocking keys or even welds are used to secure the clamping plates. In a d.c. machine the laminated stator field poles are bolted to a rolled steel yoke which has much greater inherent strength than a laminated core.

The stator windings of all a.c. machines comprise conductor bars made up of hard-drawn copper subconductors which may be connected in series or parallel. Individual subconductors are covered with a paper or glass-based tape and the assembled bar is overtaped with a similar material impregnated on older designs with bitumen but nowadays with epoxy resins, see Figure 2.4. In the portion of the conductor bar embedded in the stator slot the insulation system is compacted by being heated and pressed or it may be impregnated under vacuum and pressure. In the end winding portion where one coil is connected to another the insulation system is not compacted and may be slightly altered, containing less impregnant, so that it is more flexible and therefore better able to withstand the large electromagnetic forces which that part of the winding experiences. An important part of the construction is the manner of the bracing of these end windings. They are usually pulled back onto rigid insulated brackets, made of impregnated laminate or steel, using nylon or terylene lacing cord as in Figure 2.3. On the largest machines bracing rings of glass reinforced plastic are used with insulating bolts. The exact nature of the bracing depends upon the machine rating and the relative length of the end winding, as determined by the number of pole pairs.

The yoke (or stator core) is fitted into a frame and enclosure. On smaller machines and those of standard design the stator core is secured directly into a simplified design of a machine main

Figure 2.3 : Typical large electrical machine stator
(Courtesy of CEGB)

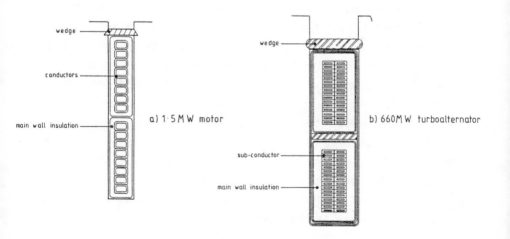

Figure 2.4 : Cross section through motor and
generator conductor bars

frame, but on larger machines the core has its own inner frame which is separate from the outer frame so that the clamped core can be removed from the enclosure for repair.

The machine enclosure can take a wide variety of forms, depending on the manner in which the machine is cooled, and the protection it needs from the environment in which it will work. Where a pressurised gas system of cooling is used the enclosure will be a thick-walled pressure vessel but for simple air-cooling with an open air circuit the enclosure will consist of thin-walled ducting. Typical enclosures are shown in Figure 2.5. There is an increasing demand nowadays to reduce the noise level from electrical machines and, apart from affecting the basic design of the stator and rotor cores, this may require specially designed noise-proof enclosures.

Electrical connections are made to the windings via copper busbars or cable which leave the machine enclosure through bushings into a terminal box. The busbars may be lightly insulated to protect them against the environment. The bushings usually consist of the busbar embedded into an epoxy resin casting, although wound paper bushings may be used on older machines. The electrical connections are well braced to withstand the large electromagnetic forces that are developed when fault currents flow. The terminal enclosure allows the proper termination of the supply cables, or busbars, and must be specially designed to suit the environment in which the machine works. For example special enclosures are required for motors which operate in inflammable areas and these incorporate baffles and seals to ensure that any flashover in the enclosure does not ignite gas, or vapour, outside the terminal box.

Many machines incorporate brushgear for connection to the rotor windings either through steel or copper sliprings or through a copper commutator. The commutator is a very carefully designed component in which copper segments interlock with the rotor so that they can withstand the bursting forces acting upon them. Also each segment must be well insulated from its neighbours, and mica is normally used for this purpose. Sliprings are usually shrunk onto an insulating sleeve mounted on a boss on the rotor shaft, and electrical connections to the sliprings are insulated and carefully braced to withstand the centrifugal forces upon them. Brushes will be springloaded and mounted in brass brush boxes, around the periphery of the rings or commutator.

Heat exchangers for the cooling system of the machine are mounted on the enclosure or may be a part of it as shown in Figure 2.5. They may be as simple as a finned casing to the machine to promote convective heat transfer to the surrounding air or they may be a more complex water-cooled system through which the cooling gas or air is ducted.

These descriptions show the very wide range of materials that are used in an electrical machine and Table 2.3 gives a summary of these. In particular it should be noted how much insulating material is present.

2.3 THE CONSTRUCTION OF DIFFERENT TYPES OF ELECTRICAL MACHINES

The previous section has provided a brief description of the major constructional components of an electrical machine and the materials of which they are made. Deterioration of performance or failure in service can occur due to damage in any of these components, and the descriptions of failures at the end of the chapter show how wide-ranging these initiating failure mechanisms can be. However, experience shows that some parts are under particular stress, and to a large extent those parts depend on the size and type of the machine. Table 2.4 gives a range of typical sizes for electrical machines.

Figure 2.5 : Typical enclosures for electrical machines
(Courtesy of Laurence, Scott & Electromotors Ltd.)

The major types of electrical machine are set out in Table 2.5, which also shows the main constructional features of those machines and the factors most likely to lead to faults.

TABLE 2.3   MATERIALS USED IN THE CONSTRUCTION
OF ELECTRICAL MACHINES

Main Component	Sub-components	Material
Enclosure	Enclosure Heat-exchanger Electrical connections Bushings	Fabricated steel Copper or brass tubing Copper or aluminium Cast epoxy resin or rolls
Stator core	Frame Core Clamp	Structural steel Electrical steel laminations or rolled steel yoke Non-magnetic, low conductivity alloy
Stator winding	Conductors Insulation End winding bracing Cooling system	Hard-drawn copper Mica-paper impregnated with bitumen, or mica-paper Impregnated laminate or steel brackets with terylene cord lacing, or srbp & glass reinforced rings & conformable epoxy bags Copper pipes, ptfe hoses
Rotor winding	Conductors Insulation	Hard-drawn copper, or copper nickel high temperature alloy, or aluminium Mica-paper & impregnant, or phenolic impregnated linen, or glassweave sheet, or no insulation

TABLE 2.3 (contd.)

Main Component	Sub-components	Material
Rotor	Body	Steel forging, or electrical steel laminations on hub, or fabricated steel spider with detachable steel pole shoes
	Bearings	Rolling element, or sleeve-type bearings
	Commutator	Copper segments & mica insulation
	Sliprings	Steel, or brass, or copper
	Brushgear	Carbon, or copper brushes with brass brushholders

2.4 THE RELATIONSHIP BETWEEN MACHINE SPECIFICATION AND FAILURE MECHANISM

Many defects occur because machines are incorrectly specified for the application to which they are being applied. For example a machine may be underpowered or have an inadequate enclosure. The specification of a machine must ensure that it is of an appropriate design for the use to which it is being put. It is a waste of time applying sophisticated monitoring techniques to a machine which is unfit for its purpose. Far better to cut-out the monitoring and change the machine for one which is more suited to the application. By the same token many operational problems could obviously be avoided by using an overdesigned machine. For example, in a hot environment it may be better to use an overrated machine, which has a substantial design margin, than push an adequately designed machine to its limit. On the

TABLE 2.4   TYPICAL SIZES AND WEIGHTS OF ELECTRICAL MACHINES

	Typical rating	Typical speed rev/min	Typical overall machine length m	Typical overall machine height m	Typical rotor weight tonnes	Typical stator weight tonnes
Turbine-type generator	660 MW	3000	12.0	4.0	80	250
Hydro-type generator	313 MW	500	9.0	5.0	434	357
Large induction motor	8 MW	1480	4.0	3.5	6	14
Large synchronous motor	9 MW	1000	5.0	4.0	8	15
A.C. commutator motor	1530/ 900 kW	1025/ 875	4.0	3.0	2	6

other hand, it is sometimes an operational fact-of-life, especially with an expensive machine, that it must continue to be
operated even though it suffers from defects due to shortcomings
in the original specifications.   In such cases effective
monitoring can help to ease the burdens placed upon the
maintenance engineer.

The specification of a machine must reflect the mechanical,
electrical and environmental conditions in which the machine will
work.   These matters will have a bearing on the mechanisms by
which the machine may fail in service.   The need for monitoring
and the selection of the parameters to be monitored must be
affected by these operational conditions.   Table 2.6 sets out the
operational conditions which are covered by a specification and

TABLE 2.5   TYPES OF ROTATING ELECTRICAL MACHINE

Main type	Sub-types	Main constructional features	Factors which may lead to faults
Synchronous generators	Steam turbine driven	Large size c. 100-1300 MW Long and thin High rotational speed Closed-circuit hydrogen-cooling Water-cooled stator windings	Damage following relay operation likely to be severe Balance problems Gas cooling circuit sealing problems Water cooling circuit sealing defects Insulation defects Sub-conductor defects Stator end winding bracing problems High centrifugal forces on rotor Rotor end bell integrity problems Enclosed casing and high strategic importance mean difficult to inspect frequently
	Water turbine driven	Large size c. 100-1300 MW Short and fat Vertically mounted Low rotational speed	Damage following relay operation likely to be severe Insulation defects associated with high voltage and air cooling Rotor pole integrity problems Thrust bearing problems Enclosed casing and high strategic importance mean difficult to inspect frequently

TABLE 2.5 (contd.)

Main type	Sub-types	Main constructional features	Factors which may lead to faults
Synchronous motors	Engine driven	Medium size Closed-circuit air-cooled Brushless	As above but on lesser scale
		Large size Excitation source d.c. exciter static excitation brushless excitation Starting by pony motor or pole face windings	High centrifugal forces on exciting winding and poles Defects in the excitation system Defects in slip rings and brushless machines Otherwise defects as synchronous generators
Induction motors	Squirrel cage rotor	All sizes Cage design of rotor Closed circuit air-cooled usually Direct on-line starting	Short air gap, possibility of eccentricity Rotor cage defects Large currents and large winding forces during starting Stator end winding bracing problems
	Slipring or wound rotor	All sizes Wound rotor Closed circuit air-cooled usually Speed variation by varying resistance connected to rotor windings	Short air-gap possibility of eccentricity High stresses on rotor winding overhang Rotor winding defects

TABLE 2.5 (contd.)

Main type	Sub-types	Main constructional features	Factors which may lead to faults
DC Machines	Traction generators	Speed variation sometimes obtained by injection of secondary emf at slip-ring	Slip-ring and brushgear defects Unbalance of rotor resistances Defects in secondary emf injection system
		Medium size Driven at variable speed Tractor duty Commutator	Commutator defects Brushgear defects Carbon dust Control gear defects
	Traction motors	Medium size Variable speed drives Traction duty Mounted close to drive wheels Commutator Motor control equipment is needed	Intermittent duty Occasional severe overloads Commutator defects Brushgear defects Carbon dust Control gear defects High mechanical shock loading Difficult to inspect frequently
AC Commutator motors	Series-wound Shunt-wound Schrage type	All sizes Variable speed drives Traction duty	Commutator defects Brushgear defects Defects with associated regulators Control gear defects

which are relevant to monitoring. These operational conditions are described in Werninck [2.4], and more details about machine specifications are given by Bone and Schwarz in [2.5].

TABLE 2.6   OPERATIONAL CONDITIONS, DEFINED IN THE
SPECIFICATION, WHICH AFFECT THE FAILURE
MECHANISMS

Operational Condition	Nature of that Condition	Effects on Failure Mechanism
Mechanical	Characteristics of the load or driving machine	Duty cycle: Successive overloads may cause overheating or bearing damage Pulsating load: May cause bearing damage Repeated starting: Repeated application of high starting forces may damage end windings and rotor windings Load or drive vibration: May be transmitted to machine causing bearing damage
Electrical	Characteristics of the electrical system and of the machine being connected to it	Slow voltage fluctuations: May cause loss of power and stalling of a motor Fast voltage fluctuations: May cause insulation failure in winding
Environmental	Characteristics of the process in which the machine is being used	Temperature: High temperature may cause insulation deterioration; low temperatures cause frosting

TABLE 2.6 (contd.)

Operational Condition	Nature of that Condition	Effects on Failure Mechanism
	Characteristics of the geographical location of the process	Humidity: High humidity may cause condensation and insulation failure; low humidity may cause dryout of solvents in insulation Cleanliness: Dirt from the environment may enter machine and contaminate insulation or mechanical components; dirt from the machine brushgear may do the same

Mechanically, machines can be exposed to periods of intermittent running, frequent starting and to arduous duty cycles, where the load varies frequently between no-load and full-load with occasional overloads. These can lead to slackening of windings, commutator and brushgear damage, insulation degradation, bearing wear and vibration. Similarly a machine driving a pulsating load such as a compressor is going to experience heavy bearing wear.

From an electrical supply point of view a machine, by virtue of its location in a supply system or its task in a manufacturing process, may be subjected to a variety of transients at its supply terminals. These may be slow fluctuations in the supply voltage or even unbalance between the three phases which can cause operational problems, for example, if the machine does not have the thermal capacity to deal with the overheating that unbalance can lead to. More rapid transients in the supply voltage, however, can overstress the winding insulation because the electric stress is not uniformly distributed throughout the winding length. Modern interrupters produce very rapid voltage surges which have been known to break down the interturn insulation on the line end coils of motors. The most severe electrical transients a machine can receive, however, are during starting or re-switching of the supply, and part of the duty of many machines in industrial processes is to be repeatedly started and run for short periods. This will cause overheating, slackening of winding systems, movement of electrical connections and overstressing of terminal boxes.

Environmentally there are thermal and contamination problems. The machine may run exceptionally hot, because of cooling problems, ambient conditions or simply that the machine is being operated to its rating limit. These can deteriorate its insulating materials. The machine may be operating in a dirty environment either because of the industrial process in which it is working, such as a textile or paper works, or because it has brushgear which produces carbon dust. If dirt can enter the main coolant circuit it may contaminate windings, bushings and electrical connections causing a deterioration in insulation integrity. Or it may foul coolers, seals, or bearings causing overheating and mechanical damage. The cooling gas may also become damp because of ambient conditions, for instance in a tropical country, or due to cooler leakage. Either of these can lead to the condensation of moisture on the electrical insulation and connections giving a reduced insulation resistance.

Clearly a machine needs to be designed to meet the environmental, mechanical and electrical disturbances it is likely to encounter during its life but any monitoring scheme which is installed should be directed towards detecting the untoward effects of these disturbances.

2.5 FAILURE MECHANISMS

From the preceding sections it can be seen that the means by which electrical machines fail depends on the type of machine and the environment in which it is working. However, it is possible to identify certain basic failure mechanisms that apply to all machines. We must then identify the early indicators of these faults because it is by detecting these that monitoring becomes possible and beneficial.

Any failure involves a route or mechanism, progressing the initial defect to the failure itself. The time taken for such a progression will vary, depending on a wide range of circumstances. What is important, however, is that all faults will have early indicators of their presence and it is here that monitoring must seek to look and act. Also any fault is likely to have a number of possible causes and is likely to give rise to a number of early indications. A typical route to failure is shown in Figure 2.6. A detailed schedule of failure mechanisms for electrical machines is given in Appendix I (p.50) where the causes and early indicators are laid out. By a study of Appendix I one can identify what parameters should be worth monitoring in order to give an early indication of a particular fault.

2.6 FAILURES ON REAL MACHINES

We have attempted in the previous section to give a general description of the ailments with which electrical machines are afflicted. However, a general view fails to give the reader a clear idea of what faults he is likely to encounter on his machines, largely because the list is taken out of context. To complete this chapter therefore we propose to describe some machine failures which draw out many of the factors that need to be considered in any monitoring system. Most of these incidents

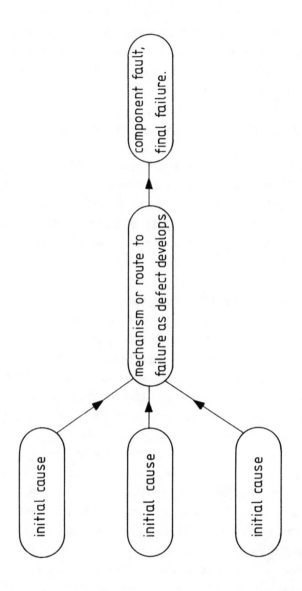

Figure 2.6 : Typical route to failure in an electrical machine

have been taken from the authors' and their colleagues' experience, so detailed references do not exist. However, various electrical machine users have tried valiantly to record their own failure statistics and a typical result is summarised in reference [2.6].

2.6.1 Stator Core Defects (generators and motors):

A core fault is a rare event which usually only occurs in the largest turbine-driven generators where the laminated steel cores are sufficiently massive, and carry a sufficiently high magnetic flux density, that when shorting occurs between laminations potentially damaging currents can flow. A number of large generators worldwide have experienced this problem, mainly as a result of damage to the bore of their stator cores during manufacture or rotor insertion, when laminations became shorted together. The construction of the cores may be such that the laminations are also firmly joined together at the core back where the core was held in its frame. Progressively, over a period of time, the circulating currents flowing through the core bore reached such large values that melting of the core-plate steel took place. The molten steel then ran into the stator slots burning through the winding insulation. The machines finally tripped on operation of the stator winding earth fault relay, by which time the damage was sufficiently severe for the stator core and winding to be written-off. The early indications of the fault were the flow of large circulating currents, high temperatures and the pyrolysing of insulation material. On smaller machines similar damage can occur. Here the damage may be the result of defects in manufacture but more often is caused by excessive vibration in the machine, leading to the fretting of stator core laminations, or it may be due to an earlier bearing failure allowing the rotor to touch-down onto the stator and rub the laminations.

2.6.2 <u>Winding Insulation Defects</u> (all machines):

At the beginning of this Chapter it was made clear that one of the intrinsically weakest components of an electrical machine, both mechanically and electrically, is the insulation system and in the earliest days of machine construction insulation faults were excessively frequent. Modern techniques of winding manufacture, however, using thermosetting, epoxy mica or vacuum pressure impregnated insulation, provide systems that are mechanically tough and electrically sound. Nonetheless, machine users are often concerned to demonstrate that the integrity of the insulation systems in their machines remains intact. There have been very few incidents of failures on the larger machines due simply to ageing of insulation. An exception to this is on air-cooled highly-rated hydro-generators where epoxy mica insulation has failed due to erosion of the insulation in the slot portion as a result of discharge activity. This was primarily a consequence of the rigidity of epoxy mica systems. Failures due to isolated insulation defects do occur frequently, however. These have taken place due to manufacturing defects, such as voids or foreign bodies, embedded in the main wall insulation, or penetration of the insulation by foreign material, such as oil or metal, from elsewhere in the machine. Whether insulation failure occurs due to ageing or the action of an isolated defect, the indications are similar in that there will be an increase in discharge activity in the machine. Insulation failures also occur from time-to-time on the bushings which carry the electrical connections out of the generator casing. On a turbine-type machine these are mounted in the pressure-tight casing and therefore have to withstand the operating pressure of the machine. Failure of a bushing can occur either due to mechanical stresses or vibration on the conductor passing through the bushing, causing it to crack, or debris being deposited on the exposed surfaces allowing it to track electrically. Again the early indication is an increase in discharge activity.

2.6.3 Winding Subconductor Faults (generators):

These faults are again generally confined to large generators where the electrical loadings are such that the stator winding is very highly stressed, electrically, thermally and mechanically. It is normal to subdivide the conductor into a large number of subconductors and to insulate and transpose them to minimise winding losses. In the most modern machines the transposition is distributed throughout the conductor length employing the Roebel technique. This gives a uniform current distribution and minimises the voltages between subconductors. Older machines, however, have the transpositions made in tne end winding at the knuckle joint and quite large voltages, up to 50 volts rms, can exist between subconductors. If severe, mechanical movement of the winding occurs during operation and the subconductor insulation fails then subconductors can short together causing arcing. A number of older machines have failed in the UK and USA due to this arcing, which in the worst cases has eroded and melted other subconductors, pyrolysing the main wall insulation of the conductor bar. If this happens in the slot portion, or near to other earthed metalwork, then an earth fault can occur but if not, it is possible for the debris, ejected from the burnt area, to produce a conducting path between electrical phases of the winding leading to the more serious phase-to-phase fault. Subconductor arcing has also been initiated by fatigue failure of subconductors, where the conductor bar emerges from the core or enters a water box, due to excessive and winding vibration. The consequences of such a failure are very similar to those of a subconductor short. When this arcing takes place in a machine with hollow water-cooled subconductors, perforation of a subconductor occurs and, since they are usually arranged so that there is an excess of cooling gas pressure over the water, this leads to a leakage of gas into the water cooling system.

The early indicators of such faults are arcing activity within the winding and the pyrolysing of insulation. Although the fact that burning is taking place deep within a conductor bar usually means that, initially at least, only small quantities of particulate and gaseous matter produced by the burning are released into the cooling gas circuit. Where water-cooled subconductors are present the fault causes a leakage of gas into the winding cooling system.

2.6.4 Stator End Winding Faults (all machines):

A considerable amount of effort over the whole range of machines has gone into the design of end winding structures. The first objective is to restrain the end winding against the large forces on the winding during transient loading and the second is to cushion the conductor bars against the smaller forces during steady, continuous running. End winding movements are larger on the older, less rigid, bituminous mica insulation system but then that system, because of its softness, is more able to withstand the steady fretting action of normal running than the hard epoxy-mica systems. In either case end winding movements in normal operation are quite significant and can be as much as a few millimetres on a large turbogenerator. Faults occur in the end winding when the bracing structure slackens, either as a result of a succession of unusual overloads or because of an extended period of continuous running. In some cases the end winding insulation becomes cracked, fretted or worn away. On the largest machines fatigue failure of conductors can occur when the winding becomes slack enough to permit a significant amount of conductor movement during normal operation or during the much larger forces of starting or re-switching.

Foreign bodies inside a machine, such as steel washers, nuts or small portions of insulation, get thrown around by the rotor. Damage is caused by these objects, usually in the stator end winding region, where the insulation is damaged by impact or eroded by debris worming into it under the action of electromagnetic forces.

The early indications of problems are an increase in end winding vibration and the possibility of electrical discharge activity to nearby earth planes.

2.6.5 Water Coolant Faults (all machines):

In water-cooled machines it is possible for a coolant blockage to occur, either in the pipework leading to or from the conductor bars or in a subconductor itself. This can be the result of pipework debris being circulated in the water system, although it should be removed by filters fitted close to the inlet of the machine. It can also be caused by gas entrainment in the water system resulting in gas-locking in coolant pathways. Sometimes in water-cooled winding machines this is associated with damage due to subconductor arcing. In either event coolant blockage will eventually lead to machine overheating and ultimately the burning of insulation. It is possible, however, to operate machines with some blocked pathway if restrictions on load are acceptable. The normal vibration of a machine in service can excite resonances in an improperly designed cooling pipework system and this can cause fatigue failure of a pipe and loss of coolant.

The early indications of these kinds of fault are high indicated conductor or cooling water temperatures, possible gas release from the water system and pyrolysing insulation leading eventually to damaging discharge activity which will be electrically detectable at the machine terminals.

2.6.6 <u>Rotor Winding Faults</u> (induction motors):

Defects on the rotor windings of induction motors have not been easy to detect because there is not always an electrical connection to the winding and it is difficult to measure the low frequency currents induced there. Although the rotor winding of a squirrel cage induction motor is exceptionally rugged, defects do occur particularly on the larger machines. These are usually associated with the high temperatures attained in the rotor, and the high centrifugal loadings on the end rings of the cage, particularly during starting. Faults may occur during manufacture, through defective casting in the case of die cast rotors, or poor jointing in the case of brazed or welded end rings. Such a defect results in a high resistance which will overheat and at high temperature the strength of the cage will be impaired. Cracking may then occur in the rotor bar and indeed usually takes place at the cage end rings where the bars are unsupported by the rotor core. Similar defects have occurred because of differential movement, of the cage in the rotor slots, because of a succession of periods of high temperature running and shutdowns. This can lead to distortion and ultimately cracking of the end rings and the associated bars. It should be remembered that the bars must provide the braking and accelerating forces on the end ring when the motor changes speed. If the motor speed fluctuates, because of changing load or as part of the normal duty cycle, then high-cycle fatigue failures can occur at the joints between bars and ring. If the motor is repeatedly started then the exceptional starting forces may lead to low-cycle fatigue failure of the winding component. The early indications of these faults are pulsations in the speed, supply current and stray leakage flux of the machine.

The rotor windings on wound rotor induction motors are of rather similar design to the stator winding of the motor except that the end windings are restrained against centrifugal forces by steel end rings or more commonly woven glass fibre bands. Damage to the windings usually occurs in the end region due to centrifugal forces on the crossovers and connections of the winding causing shorts between turns. These faults are similar to the problems experienced on the rotor windings of high-speed turbine-type generators. An additional difficulty encountered with the wound rotor machine is that of ensuring balance between the phases of the external resistors connected to the winding via the slip rings. If the resistors are unbalanced then the currents flowing in the rotor windings will be unbalanced and overheating will occur. This can lead to the rapid degradation of rotor winding insulation and ultimately failure such as is shown in Figure 2.7. The problem is difficult to detect because the rotor currents are at the very low slip frequency and one must detect relatively small differences between those currents.

2.6.7 Rotor Winding Faults (generators):

In turbine-type generators the rotor winding insulation and bracing system must be designed to withstand the exceptionally high centrifugal forces imposed upon them, and the faults are usually associated with these forces. A short can occur between rotor turns, due to cracking of the winding insulation. The shorting current which then flows creates a local hot-spot leading to further insulation degradation and the possibility of further shorted turns. Once a short has occurred there is an asymmetry in the flux in the machine and an unbalanced force on the rotor which causes rotor vibrations. This is usually the first evidence that a shorted turn is present. Shorts are also sometimes promoted by copper dust produced by fretting action in the rotor winding. This occurs because of the cyclic movement which a large winding experiences relative to the rotor, partly due to self-weight bending of the long thin rotor and partly due to thermal cycling. If an insulation fault occurs between the winding and the rotor body then an earth fault current flows which can be detected by an earth leakage relay. The earth fault current is limited so that a single earth fault is not serious but if a second earth fault occurs then very large circulating currents can flow. Indeed on some occasions an arc has been struck at the earth fault not only causing damage to the winding and its insulation but also severely damaging the rotor forging.

The early indications of these faults are a distortion of the air gap flux and associated stray leakage flux around the machine and an increase in bearing vibration.

2.6.8   Rotor Body Defects (all machines):

The high centrifugal stresses in machine rotors can also lead to problems in the rotor body as well as the windings. The propagation of cracks from surface defects in the rotor material, or its associated components, due to high-cycle fatigue under the action of the self-weight forces during rotation, has led to catastrophic rotor failure. This situation is exacerbated if the cooling gas contains moisture or other impurities which encourage corrosion and can lower the resistance of the rotor material to fatigue failure. Excessive heating of the rotor can also weaken the rotor material and there have been a number of incidents, particularly on large generators, where eddy current losses in the rotor due to negative sequence in the supply has led to overheating and the initiation of serious fatigue cracking. But it is not only high-cycle fatigue which can cause a rotor to fail. Large transients on the electrical system to which a machine is connected can also impose sudden strains on its rotor. If a resonant condition exists between the machine and the system then sudden transients can excite torsional oscillations which can lead to rotor or coupling failure and this has occurred in many motors and at least one large generator.

Figure 2.7 : Failure of a wound rotor induction motor
(Courtesy of CEGB)

Eccentricity of the rotor can lead to vibration due to unbalanced magnetic pull and this can be compounded when the asymmetric heating leads to thermal bending of the rotor. Two and four pole totally enclosed machines are particularly prone to these problems especially if they have a short air-gap.

The early indications of these types of fault are usually excessive transverse bearing vibrations although attention is being focussed more recently on measuring the torsional oscillations of the shaft itself.

2.7 CONCLUSION

In this Chapter we have given a flavour of how electrical machines are built, how they are operated and typically how they fail in service. The failure mechanisms demonstrate how defects may be detected in their early stages by monitoring appropriate parameters. In the next Chapters we will describe the monitoring techniques which are available to give us that early warning.

APPENDIX I   FAILURE MECHANISMS IN ELECTRICAL MACHINES

Fault	Causes	Early Indicators of The Fault
MACHINE ENCLOSURE		
Cooling System		
Failure of conductor cooling hoses	Defective materials Impact damage during installation Impact damage in service Electrical breakdown Shock due to fault close up to machine Mechanical vibration	Increased moisture level Overheating of conductor bar Pyrolysed insulation
Failure of cooling pipework	Defective materials Corrosion due to impurities in cooling water Defective installation Mechanical vibration	Increased temperatures Increased moisture level Pyrolysed insulation
Leak in heat exchanger	Defective materials Corrosion due to impurities in cooling water Defective installation	Increased moisture level
Bushings and electrical connections		
Electrical failure of a bushing	Defective manufacture Contamination leading to breakdown Mechanical vibration leading to fracture	Electrical discharge activity
Failure of electrical connection	Defective installation, slack joints Mechanical vibration leading to slack joints Mechanical vibration leading to fracture	Electrical arcing activity Circulating currents
Flashover in connections or terminal box	Defective design Contamination leading to breakdown Mechanical vibration leading to fracture	Electrical arcing activity
STATOR CORE		
Laminations		
Core hot spot	Defective manufacture Debris between laminations from manufacture Debris in core bore Damage on insertion of rotor Fretting of core plate insulation due to slackening Damage to bearings causing a rotor rub	Increased temperatures Pyrolysed insulation

Fault	Causes	Early Indicators of The Fault
Core slackening	Defective assembly giving inadequate compression Failure of clamping mechanism Excessive mechanical vibration Failure of core duct spacers	Electrical discharge activity Pyrolysed insulation
Frame		
Frame vibration	Defective design Defective installation Excessive mechanical vibration	Vibration
Circulating currents	Defective manufacture Defective installation	Increased temperatures Pyrolysed insulation
Loss of coolant	Blocked subconductors Broken hose Faulty pumps	Electrical discharge activity Increased moisture level Increased temperatures Pyrolysed insulation
Earth faults	Any of damage described for slot portion above	Electrical discharge Circulating currents Distorted air gap flux Stray fluxes
Turn-to-turn faults	Surges in electrical supply system Any of the damage described here	
ROTOR WINDINGS		
Earth faults	Abrasion of insulation Abrasion of conductors producing metal dust Thermal cycling due to excessive starting	Vibration Earth leakage current Pyrolysed insulation
Turn-to-turn faults	Abrasion of insulation Abrasion of conductors producing metal dust Thermal cycling due to excessive starting	Distorted air gap flux Stray fluxes Vibration Circulating currents Earth leakage current Pulsating speed Pulsating supply current Pyrolysed insulation
Broken winding	Defective design Defective manufacture Faulty joints Thermal cycling due to excessive starting	Electrical arcing activity Pyrolysed insulation Distorted air gap flux Stray fluxes Vibration Pulsating speed Pulsating supply current

Fault	Causes	Early Indicators of The Fault
ROTOR BODY		
Integrity failure of body or wedges	Defective rotor forging or fabrication Defective design of wedges Thermal cycling due to excessive starting Thermal cycling due to negative-sequence Over-torque due to close up fault Over-torque due to drive defect	Cracks found by NDT Vibration
Mechanical or thermal unbalance	Movement of winding or end-rings Loss of material on rotor Asymmetric blocking of cooling ducts Shorted turns on rotor	Vibration
Mechanical misalignment	Defective installation Failure of bearings	Distorted air gap flux Stray fluxes Vibration Circulating currents Overheating when rub occurs
STATOR WINDINGS		
End winding portion		
Local damage to insulation	Impact damage during installation Impact damage during service Shock due to fault close up to machine Movement due to repeated starting	Electrical discharge activity
Fretting of insulation	Defective design of bracing Slackening due to frequent starting Poor maintenance resulting in slackening Contamination by oil	End winding vibration Electrical discharge activity
Contamination of insulation by moisture, oil or dirt	High humidity in cooling gas Imperfect oil seals on machine enclosure Inadequate enclosure	Increased moisture level Oil mist Particulates in cooling gas
Damage to connectors	Defective installation, slack joints Slack joints Impact damage in service Mechanical vibration leading to slack joints Mechanical vibration leading to fracture	Electrical discharge activity
Cracking of insulation	Defective design at bracing Shock due to fault close up to machine High temperatures Low humidity in cooling gas	End winding vibration Electrical discharge activity

Fault	Causes	Early Indicators of The Fault
Discharge erosion of insulation	Inadequate stress-grading at core end Delamination of insulation Defective manufacture	Electrical discharge activity
Displacement of con-ductors	Shock due to fault close up to machine	End winding vibration
Turn-to-turn faults	Any of the damage described for end windings above	Electrical discharge activity Circulating currents Distorted air gap flux Stray fluxes
Slot portion		
Fretting of insulation	Slack slot wedges Slack core laminations	Electrical discharge activity
Displacement of con-ductors	Defective design of wedging system Shock due to fault close up to machine	Leak in coolant water system
BEARINGS AND SEALS		
Misalignment	Misalignment with drive Incorrect bearing clearances Incorrect bearing loading	Damage found by inspection Vibration Debris in lubricating oil
Loss of lubrication	Contamination of lubricating oil Loss of lubricating oil Excessive bearing clearance	Damage found by inspection Vibration Debris in lubricating oil
Electrical activity	Failure of earthing brush Failure of pedestal insulation	Damage found by inspection Altered shaft voltages Stray fluxes Vibration
Failure of bearing	Any of the damage from bearing problems above	
Failure of seal	Misalignment on installation Contamination oil supply Magnetised seal Imperfect fitting	Gas leakage from machine Oil ingress to machine Altered shaft votlages Stray fluxes Overheating

Fault	Causes	Early Indicators of The Fault
COMMUTATORS, SLIP RINGS AND BRUSH GEAR		
Disrupted commutator	Defective maintenance Defective manufacture Overheating due to excessive overloads Overheating due to improperly seated brushes Excessive sparking due to ineffective compoles Excessive sparking due to humidity of air	Sparking at brushgear
Damaged slip rings	Defective maintenance Imperfect cooling Imperfect seating of brushes leading to scoring Failure of slip ring insu- lation Movement of slip ring	Sparking Uneven current distri- bution in brushes Brush wear
Damaged brush gear	Defective maintenance Improper brush pressure Imperfect cooling Wrong brush grade	Sparking Uneven current distri- in brushes Brush wear
AUXILIARY EQUIPMENT		
Damage to external supplies	Various	Miscellaneous
Damage to regulators associated with machine	Various	Miscellaneous

CHAPTER 3

The Elements of
A Monitoring System

3.1 FUNCTIONAL DESCRIPTION

A commitment to condition monitoring involves the operators of plant in the conduct of a range of activities. These activities may be complicated in nature and indeed may often be performed automatically under computer control. They can, however, always be broken down into a relatively small number of easily identifiable functional tasks. This makes it much easier to identify the common elements of machine condition monitoring schemes; irrespective of system complexity. In essence we are saying that the engineer making and examining the occasional list of meter readings, with a view to producing some operational or maintenance stratagem, is involved in a procedure that has much that is identifiably similar in function to the working of a complicated and sophisticated monitoring system. Such systems may multiplex inputs from literally hundreds of transducers and perform mathematically and logically complex operations to reduce and process the acquired data. The power of modern microprocessors is now sufficiently developed to allow the use of expert system techniques to recommend appropriate actions in response to interrogation of the monitored data base.

In view of the above arguments we believe that the following functional tasks are essential before a process can be thought of as condition monitoring. They are:

(i)   the transduction task (primary signal
       collection);
(ii) the data acquisition task;
(iii) the processing task;
(iv) the diagnostic task (reporting phase acting
       on the processed data).

At each stage human intervention is possible, and often
desirable. Indeed in many cases some of these 4 tasks may be
wholly carried out by the operator. For example let us return to
our example of the engineer collecting his meter readings, and
try to identify each of the above tasks. The meter deflections
will naturally be in response to measurements made elsewhere in
the system, and may be picked up by CT's or VT's, or accelerometers for example. This is obviously the transduction task, and
is normally performed automatically for it is difficult for the
human operator to act in anything but a qualitative way in
fulfilment of this task. That is, he may be able to tell if one
piece of plant is hotter than another, or noiser, but little
else.

The data acquisition task can be identified with the action of
the engineer in writing down the series of readings from each
meter, together with information regarding the time, location,
and loading condition perhaps, of the plant. In our example this
is wholly under human control.

The processing task corresponds to the analysis of the readings
in some way. It may be considered appropriate to average several
of the readings for example, and to present them in a way that
allows easy comparison with other data. This phase can vary
greatly in complexity, and it is this task that demands the
application of significant computing power in automatic systems.

We shall return to many of the more common processing techniques later merely noting at the moment the use of methods such as spectral analysis, time averaging, and auto and cross-correlation.

The diagnostic task operates on the results of the processing task in order to recommend action that hopefully will result in improved operational readiness and performance, and improved maintenance scheduling. Again, returning to our simple example, on the basis of examining the average meter readings and comparing them with manufacturers' operational limits, say, the engineer may decide that during the next plant shut down specific items of machinery must be overhauled or replaced. He arrives at this judgement on the basis of his experience and the data available to him as a result of collecting and processing the meter readings, and having access to the manufacturer's data on operating limits. The diagnostic task is still most often

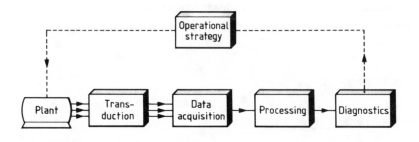

Figure 3.1 : The monitoring tasks

carried out with a significant input from the human operator, but with the development of knowledge-based, expert systems full automation of this phase may be possible, in limited situations.

In Figure 3.1 we summarise, in schematic form, these 4 tasks associated with the condition monitoring activity, and indicate the obvious step of closing the loop as an aid to operational performance.

We must now examine each of the 4 monitoring tasks in some detail, both in a general way and as they apply to electrical machines. At all times we must be mindful that the monitoring activity is aimed at reaping the benefits to be gained by closing the loop identified in Figure 3.1.

3.2 THE MONITORING TASKS

Each of the 4 tasks that we have identified are substantial areas of study in their own right. In a text of this size it is not possible to treat them in great depth and we must content ourselves with an examination of the most useful and important features of each of them, with particular reference to the needs of electrical machines. The interested reader may increase his understanding of particular aspects by referring to the references at the end of the book.

3.3   TRANSDUCTION

3.3.1 General Remarks

The transducer is a device which extracts small amounts of energy from one system, or piece of plant, and transmits it to some other system for subsequent interpretation. Implicit in this definition is the requirement for both the sensing of the primary quantity, for example current, voltage, displacement, acceleration, temperature, or pressure, and the matching of the sensor to some primary signal processing and data acquisition system.

The majority of sensors that are used in the monitoring of electrical machines will provide an output in the form of a current or a voltage that will then be conditioned by analogue or digital techniques. Whatever the detailed application may be, there are many general considerations to be met in deciding whether or not a device is fit for purpose. We shall proceed by examining in greater detail the commonest forms of transducers used when monitoring electrical machines.

3.3.2 Temperature Measurement

Temperature is a widely monitored parameter in electrical drives and generators. It is, for example, quite common to find temperature sensing used to monitor the cooling fluids of large turbogenerators, and specific areas of the stator core also. Such devices can only give indications of gross changes taking place within the machine but they are extremely effective if mounted and monitored in carefully selected sites. Bearing temperatures are commonly monitored and, together with vibration sensing, it provides the standard approach to the assessment of the condition of these elements. The techniques and sites for temperature measurement are described in Chapter 7. Here we describe the three principal methods of measuring temperature:

   (i)   thermocouples;
  (ii)   resistance temperature detection;
 (iii)   thermistors.

Each type has acceptable areas of application which we will now briefly investigate.

Temperature measurement using thermocouples is based on the well known Seebeck effect whereby a current circulates around a circuit formed using two dissimilar metals, when the metal junctions are held at different temperatures. Using a technique known as cold junction compensation, which is explained in any standard work on thermocouples, for example Reference [3.1], the need for a carefully controlled reference junction is avoided and a device with effectively only a single junction results. Thermocouples can be used to measure temperatures ranging from near to absolute zero to over 3000°C. Some typical junction materials and their associated operating ranges and outputs are given below in Table 3.1, taken from reference [3.2].

TABLE 3.1   RANGES AND OUTPUTS OF THERMOCOUPLE
JUNCTION MATERIALS

Junction Materials	Range °C	Output emf mV
Copper/Constantan	-250 - 400	20 mV at 400°C
Iron/Constantan	-200 - 850	42 mV at 750°C
Chromel/Alumel	-200 - 1100	30 mV at 750°C
Platinum/Rhodium	0 - 1400	7 mV at 750°C

The working life of such devices depends on the working temperature and the physical dimensions of the junction materials, but for copper/constantan and chromel/alumel, which are most widely used in electrical machines, they can expect to survive for many years.

The resistance temperature detector (RTD) is simply a thin-film or wire-wound device that has a reasonable, positive temperature coefficient of resistance coupled with good stability. Platinum and nickel are widely used in the construction of these devices.

In the thin-film form, platinum is evaporated on to a ceramic substrate, and suitably encapsulated they can be used at temperatures up to 600°C.   Such devices are widely used for gas temperature sensing applications.

RTD devices are constructed generally to a base resistance of 100 ohms at 0°C and have the advantage of being linear over a wide operating range.   They have a relatively low sensitivity however, and in the thin film form are subject to long term drift.   They are generally used in a 4-wire configuration with some form of Wheatstone Bridge circuitry, but 2-wire or 3-wire operation is possible.

Figure 3.2 shows a typical multichannel temperature monitoring system for surveillance of bearing lubrication oil temperatures. It is designed to accept inputs from 100 ohm, 3-wire, RTDs or

Figure 3.2 : Temperature monitoring system
(Courtesy of Weir Pumps Ltd.)

chromel/alumel thermocouples, and incorporates facilities for outputting signals to external alarms or relays on the basis of comparison with a predetermined set point value.

The final type of temperature transducer we wish to briefly mention is the thermistor. Previously we mentioned devices which alter their resistance as a function of temperature, but we noted that in such devices (RTD's) the changes involved were small. Thermistors operate in a like manner but because they are made from ceramic semiconductors, for example the metal oxides of cobalt, iron, titanium, and nickel, they show a large change in resistance as a function of temperature. They have the advantages of high stability, fast response, and very small physical size. They are generally limited to temperatures up to 300°C, for above this level stability reduces. They do not provide a linear output however and this must be taken into account. It is possible to provide such compensation as is required electronically or digitally when incorporating these devices in a monitoring system. Alternatively the thermistor may be used as a switching device to operate an alarm when the temperature exceeds a preset limit. Thermistors are inexpensive and are manufactured in a variety of forms, and can be extremely small. Typically a glass bead device will have a diameter of the order of 0.25 mm, whilst flake thermistors are produced in thicknesses down to 0.025 mm with cross-sections of 0.5 x 0.5 mm. They are also available in the form of discs, rods and washers.

3.3.3 Vibration Measurements

In chapter 6 we will discuss at length the techniques available and the applicability of vibration monitoring. Here for the sake of introduction we will say something about the types of transducers needed to effectively measure vibration. At the present time, vibration sensing, in which we also include acoustic noise measurement, is the single most important monitoring tool available to the operator of electromechanical plant. Its use is extremely widespread and has reached a high degree of sophistication. It revolves around the measurement of three related - quantities:

   (i)   displacement;
   (ii) velocity;
 (iii) acceleration.

Which quantity one should measure depends on the size of the plant being monitored, and the frequency range in which one is interested. Generally machines of similar type and size have a more or less constant vibrational velocity. Also as speed increases it is likely that displacement levels will fall, but acceleration levels will rise. This suggests that as the frequencies of interest rise it is better to progress from a displacement device to a velocity transducer, and ultimately to an accelerometer. As a guide the approximate frequency ranges of application are as shown in Figure 3.3.

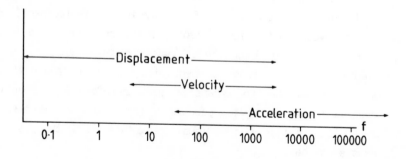

Figure 3.3 : Normal ranges of applicability for
vibration ranges

Care must be exercised, however, when monitoring systems which have small moving masses for in such circumstances transmitted forces may be small, and displacement will usually provide the best indication of condition.

We can now characterise vibration transducers according to the quantity they measure.

Displacement transducers

Here we shall confine our interests to non-contacting probes or proximeters. Such devices operate by using an h.f. source to generate an electromagnetic field at the probe tip. The system energy is thus dependent upon the local geometry of the area surrounding the probe tip. If it changes, for example when the target surface moves with respect to the probe, then the system energy also changes. This change is readily measured and is related to the displacement of the target surface from the probe tip. It should be noted that such systems measure the relative motion between the probe and the target; hence the vibration of the housing in which the probe is mounted is not readily measured by this technique.

Sensitivities of the order of 10 mV/micron displacement are easily achievable with displacement probes, and they find wide application in situations where heavy housings ensure small external movements. The measurements of eccentricity and differential movements due to expansion are therefore most easily achieved using proximity transducers. They can also be effectively applied to measure rotational speed by sensing the passage of keyways on shafts.

As mentioned previously displacement is most effectively measured at the lower frequencies even though the frequency range of eddy current systems can extend above 10 kHz. They are

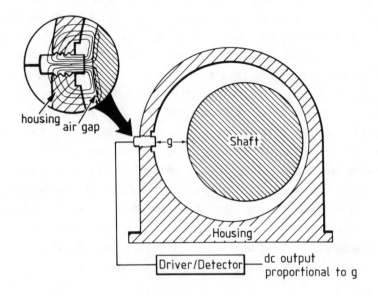

Figure 3.4 : Operation of the proximity probe

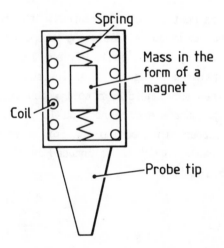

Figure 3.5 : Principle of the velocity probe

relatively robust transducers and the driving and detection circuits are straightforward. Essentially the h.f. signal applied to the probe is modulated by the passage of the target, and the demodulated signal used as the measurement quantity. Consideration of Figure 3.4, which illustrates the basic displacement measurement principle, shows us that the output of the system will depend not only on the displacement between the probe and the target, but also on the material from which the target is made. This is because the eddy current reaction of the target, and hence the system energy, is dependent upon both the conductivity and permeability of the material. Proximity probes must therefore be calibrated for each target material. Care must also be taken when mounting the probe to ensure that conducting and magnetic surfaces around the probe tip do not cause unnecessary disturbance of the applied h.f. field and that the target surface is smooth with no surface or magnetic disturbances.

Velocity transducers

Velocity is most usefully measured in the range 10 Hz to 1 kHz. This can be achieved by designing a spring mass system with a natural frequency less than 10 Hz, and letting the mass take the form of a permanent magnet, as illustrated in Figure 3.5. The magnet is then surrounded by a coil which is securely attached to the housing. Whenever the housing is placed in contact with a vibrating surface the housing and coil move with respect to the magnet and cause an emf to be induced in the coil, in accordance with the expression.

$$e = \ell \underline{B} \times \underline{v} \qquad \qquad \dots (3.1)$$

where e is the induced emf, ℓ is the effective length of the conductor in the coil, $\underline{B}$ is the radially directed flux density (which is constant), and $\underline{v}$ is the velocity in the axial direction.

This transducer is relatively delicate but has the advantage of producing an output signal that is relatively large, and there-fore requires little or no signal conditioning.

Accelerometers

Nowadays, however, velocity and displacement are commonly measured using accelerometers, the required parameter being derived by integration.

Accelerometers produce an electrical output that is directly proportional to the acceleration to which they are subjected. In recent years the piezoelectric device has become almost univer-sally accepted as the transducer to use for all but the most specialised of vibration measurements. It is physically much more robust than the velocity transducer and has a much superior frequency range. This has become more important as techniques involving frequencies well above 1 kHz have been adopted.

The construction of a typical piezoelectric accelerometer is illustrated in Figure 3.6.

When it is subject to vibration, the seismic mass, which is held against the piezoelectric element, exerts a force upon it. This force is proportional to the acceleration. Under such conditions the piezoelectric element, which is usually a polarised ceramic material, generates a proportional electric charge across its faces. The output can then be conditioned using a charge amplifier and either velocity or displacement signals recovered by integration. The device has the obvious advantage of

68

generating its output without an external electrical source being required. More recently integrated circuit piezoelectric devices have become available with the output signal conditioning resident in the accelerometer encapsulation.

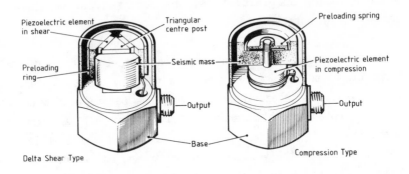

Figure 3.6 : The piezoelectric accelerometer
(Courtesy of Brüel and Kjær)

When using piezoelectric accelerometers it is important to realise that, unlike proximity probes, the natural frequency of the device is designed to be above the usual operating range. A typical frequency response is given in Figure 3.7. This limits the useful operating range to around 30% of the natural frequency. Also because the output is low at low frequencies the normal range of application of accelerometers is approximately 1 kHz to 8 kHz, although small devices may have ranges extending beyond 200 kHz. See references [3.3] and [3.4].

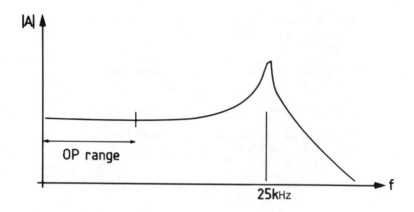

Figure 3.7 : Accelerometer response

There is an extremely wide range of piezoelectric accelerometers available today, from very small devices that will measure shocks of high acceleration, in excess of 10^6 ms^{-2}, to large devices with sensitivities greater than 1000 pC/ms^{-2}. Highly sensitive devices, on the other hand, have to be physically large so as to accommodate the increased seismic mass required to generate the high output. In all cases, however, care must be taken when mounting accelerometers since they can be easily destroyed through over-tightening.

Table 3.2 below provides a short summary of the area of application of each of the transducer types discussed above.

TABLE 3.2   APPLICATION OF VIBRATION TECHNIQUES

Application	Transducer Type
Motor/pump drives	Velocity or acceleration
Motor/fan drives	Displacement or velocity
Motor connected to gear boxes (rolling element bearings)	Acceleration
Motors with oil film bearings	Displacement
Generators/steam turbines	Displacement
Overall vibration levels on all of the above	Velocity

3.3.4 Force and Torque Transducers

Undoubtedly the two commonest ways of measuring force are with the use of the strain gauge, a simple device that comprises a long length of resistance wire securely bonded to a surface which will alter shape elastically under the action of force. When the gauge is stressed under the action of force, the cross- section and length of the wire changes so that its resistance alters. A typical arrangement for a strain gauge is shown in Figure 3.8.

If the elements have a cross-section A and a length L, the element resistance is,

$$R = \rho \frac{A}{L}$$

where ρ is the resistivity of the gauge.

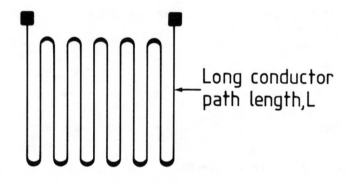

Long conductor
path length, L

Figure 3.8 : Typical arrangement of strain gauge

For a circular cross section of A, $A = \pi d^2/4$ where d is the diameter.

Hence

$$\frac{\delta R}{R} = \frac{\delta \rho}{\rho} - \frac{\delta L}{L} + \frac{2\delta d}{d}$$

therefore, multiplying by L and dividing by δL gives,

$$\frac{\delta R}{R} \cdot \frac{L}{\delta L} = \frac{\delta \rho}{\rho} \cdot \frac{L}{\delta L} - 1 + \frac{2\delta d}{d} \cdot \frac{L}{\delta L} \qquad \ldots (3.2)$$

But $\frac{\delta L}{L}$ is identified as the axial strain, ϵ_a, and $\frac{\delta d}{d}$ is the transverse strain, ϵ_t. Also $\frac{\delta d}{d} \cdot \frac{L}{\delta L}$ is the Poisson ratio of the material, ν.

The factor $\frac{\delta R}{R} \cdot \frac{L}{\delta L}$ is termed the gauge factor G; hence (3.2) becomes

$$G = \frac{\delta \rho}{\rho} \epsilon_a + 1 + 2\nu \qquad \qquad \ldots (3.3)$$

Now if the values of G and R are controlled by manufacture so that,

$$G = \frac{\delta R}{R \epsilon_a}$$
then

$$\delta R = RG\epsilon_a \qquad \qquad \ldots (3.4)$$

and the gauge can be calibrated.

In order to measure δR it is usual to place the gauge in the arm of a Wheatstone bridge network which is balanced when the element is unstressed.

In order to measure forces, strain gauges need to be applied in a particular arrangement, examples of which are shown in Figure 3.9. Force transducers of this type are routinely used to measure forces ranging from a few Newtons to many Tonnes force. Care must be taken to either operate them at a constant temperature   or properly compensate for the effects due to expansion. Modern bridge systems, to measure δR, may be self balancing with automatic read out.

It is immediately apparent that such devices can be used to measure torques applied to shafts but if the shaft is in motion the additional problem of extracting the signal must be faced.

This may be done using instrumentation grade slip rings attached to the shaft, or by suitable noise-free telemetry. Telemetry systems in the electrically noisy environment around electro-mechanical machinery can be difficult to implement.

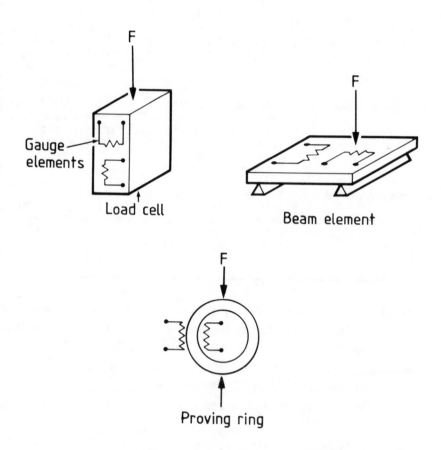

Figure 3.9 : Arrangement of strain gauges
to measure force
Taken from ref. [3.5]

Other less common types of transducer for the measurement of force are described briefly in Table 3.3, from reference [3.5].

TABLE 3.3   OTHER FORCE MEASUREMENT METHODS

Method	Principle of Operation	Remarks
Fluidic load cells	Force applied to a dia-phragm causes pressure.	Pressure signal must then be con-verted to an elec-trical output.
Fibre optic	Some optical fibres exhibit the ability to phase rotate the trans-mitted light in propor-tion to the stress applied to the fibre.	Careful phase mea-surement needed. Expensive but highly accurate.
Magneto-elastic	The magnetic properties of some ferromagnetic materials depend on the mechanical stress the material is subjected to.	Expensive but accu-rate. Special pre-cautions needed to screen devices.

In this section we have simply outlined the commonest means of measuring force, and it must be realised that it is an area that is extremely well established and highly-developed. The use of specific techniques for particular applications can be found by searching the large literature associated with free measurement. Some helpful references are provided at the end of the book.

3.3.5 Electrical and Magnetic Measurements

The basic electrical quantities associated with electromechan-ical plant are readily measured by tapping in to the existing voltage and current transformers that are always installed as part of the protection system. These are standard and therefore need not be considered further here.

There can be a requirement, however, to measure the magnetic flux density in, or around, electrical machines. This is done in one of two ways. Either a simple search coil is used, or a Hall effect device may be more appropriate. These two options are different in nature since the search coil is a passive device whereas the Hall effect device is not. On the other hand, only the search coil has the capacity for significant energy storage; therefore in areas that may present an explosion hazard their use must conform to current safety standards. These standards are well set out in Reference [3.6].

With the search coil the induced emf, e, is given by the expression,

$$e = \omega BAN \qquad \qquad \dots (3.5)$$

where ω is the frequency of the normal component of flux density, B. A is the effective cross-section of area of the coil and N the number of turns in the coil. Obviously such devices give no output with d.c. fields, and at very high frequencies the output may be limited by self-screening effects.

Coils can be produced by evaporating copper directly onto surfaces, in the appropriate position. Or by evaporating them on to insulating materials such as Mylar, which can then be bonded to the appropriate surface. These techniques are extremely useful if the coil is to be used inside an electrical machine, where the coil must not be allowed to move into the airgap and risk damage to other areas of the machine.

As previously mentioned, if the coil is to be placed in a hazardous area then it is not the output of the coil that is important, it is the possibility of an unwanted input that must be considered. The energy stored in a coil is given by the expression:

$$E = \frac{1}{2}LI^2 \qquad\qquad\qquad \dots (3.6)$$

where L is the inductance of the coil, and I the current flowing
in it. The stored energy E can be reduced by ensuring that either
L is low or I is limited. For a high signal output,L, which
is a function of N , should be reasonably high. Therefore one
must limit I. This is easily achieved by adding resistance or
ensuring that the wire from which the coil is fabricated is thin
enough to provide the required resistance. This coupled with
suitable buffering to the signal conditioning amplifier is usually
sufficient to allow operation in most areas.

The Hall effect device does not suffer from such disadvantages
so long as the required power supply to the device is suitably
isolated, but it is by nature only able to provide a measurement
of flux density over a very small area. Figure 3.10 shows the
basic principle of operation of the Hall effect element.

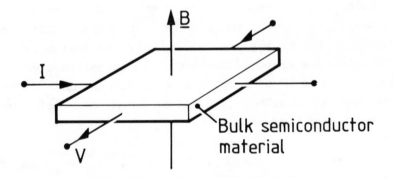

Figure 3.10 : The Hall Principle

The output voltage V is related to the applied current and field by,

$$V = \frac{kIB}{qn} \qquad \ldots (3.7)$$

where q is the electronic charge, and n is the number of charge carriers per unit volume in the semiconductor. k is a constant, and k/qn is known as the Hall constant of the material.

Hall effect devices have the advantage of being able to measure down to d.c., and can be made in extremely small sizes. They are not very robust, however, and therefore require special packaging for arduous service. They also have a non-linear temperature characteristic and the output voltage is usually linearly related to flux density over a limited range only.

3.3.6 Wear and Debris Measurement Transducers

Chemical methods of monitoring will be discussed fully in Chapter 5, later in the book. For completeness, we will briefly mention one aspect of this subject here, in so much as it relates directly to the transduction task in monitoring. It is often necessary to assess the condition of lubrication systems. The most common method of doing this is to use a so-called debris sensitive detector. Such a detector depends on the lubricating fluid being continually passed through a device that is sensitive to the presence of particulate material. This is commonly achieved using either an electrical transducer to measure electrical changes in inductance, capacitance, or conductivity, or optically by measuring changes in turbidity of the lubricant.

The principle of operation of the electrical techniques is essentially the same. The lubricant and debris pass through a small chamber which can alternatively be part of a conductive circuit, the dielectric in a capacitor, or part of a magnetic circuit, in order to measure changes in conductivity, capacitance, or inductance respectively.

All of these devices can give good indications of general levels of wear, and dramatic indications of the occasional large piece of debris. Such transducers are both complex and expensive, and require careful and regular attention.

Optical monitors generally operate by sensing either a loss of transmission of light through a test cell, or by detecting light scatter from the particulate matter (known as the Tyndall effect), as shown in Figure 3.11.

Maintenance of optical systems is minimal, and they may be used on a wide variety of fluids. They are subject to spurious output, however, if the lubricant becomes aerated to any significant degree. They are also unable to differentiate between harmful and non-harmful particulate matter.

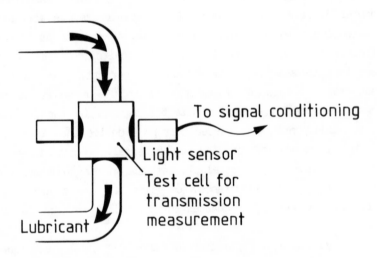

Figure 3.11 : Arrangement for an optical debris sensor

3.4 DATA ACQUISITION AND PRIMARY PROCESSING

The precise nature of the data acquisition techniques used is usually determined by the subsequent algebraic manipulations that will be performed on the data sets produced by the transduction process. It is not really possible, therefore, to separate these two tasks fully, in most cases. What is of paramount importance, however, irrespective of the complexity of the monitoring system, is the fidelity of the information received by the processing unit. Transmitted or recorded data must be sufficiently noise-free to comply with the demands of the monitoring system, and must be wholly consistent. If this is not the case then the whole data set, perhaps spanning several months, may be effectively corrupted and therefore useless. In complex systems handling many inputs, either continuously, or on a sampled basis, it is usual to have the processing system remote from the plant. In such cases some degree of local data conversion may be advisable. For example the signals taken from a group of machines in adjacent locations may be routed to a nearby collection point which digitizes the incoming signals and identifies them for onward transmission to the central system. In noisy environments it may even be desirable to digitize signals at the collection point, and then forward them to a gathering point.

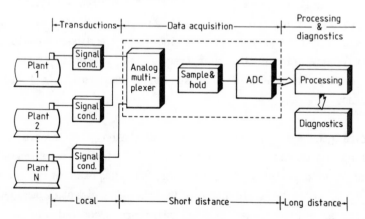

Figure 3.12 : A preferred structure for a fully automatic system

Figure 3.12 illustrates a preferred structure for a fully automatic system. The basic data acquisition system shown above is broken down into three, concatenated functions, multiplexing, sample and hold and analogue to digital conversion (ADC). The use of a multiplexer is essential if a large number of channels are to be monitored, and can be appropriate even for small numbers of channels because it allows the use of a single high quality ADC, rather than recourse to many lower grade devices. High speed multiplexers are readily available that can scan at rates in excess of 5000 channels per second. This, of course, is inappropriate when detailed time histories are needed. The price one pays for the simplification offered by multiplexing is that the monitoring is no longer truly continuous. However in most practical cases the sample cycle time, the interval between the collection of successive samples, will be very small compared with time over which fault conditions develop.

The sample and hold unit, which is essentially just a high speed amplifier that can store its input value on command, allows a constant signal to be presented to the ADC during its conversion cycle. This allows the sample time of the ADC to be significantly reduced and results in a much faster system.

The ADC unit is generally the heart of the data acquisition task and it is imperative that it is fit for purpose in terms of conversion time and accuracy. Using sample and hold, analogue to digital conversion units, input frequencies greater than 200 kHz are easily achieved, at modest cost, and to 12 bit (0.05%) accuracy.

More generally, great care must be taken with regard to the cabling and mounting of transducers and equipment. Cables should be of high quality and routed through unexposed areas wherever possible, so as to avoid the possibility of accidental damage. In most cases twin screened twisted pairs are acceptable to couple a transducer to the primary processing unit. Optical fibre cabling is now more robust and therefore an acceptable alternative, particularly when high noise immunity is essential. Communications between the primary processing unit and the processing system should be established via a high integrity low-noise link to avoid any chance of data corruption, or interruption.

3.5   THE PROCESSING TASK

3.5.1 General Remarks

Broadly speaking, the processing task is that part of the monitoring activity where data, which has been collected and suitably formatted, is operated upon or otherwise transformed so that a diagnosis of plant condition can more readily be made. As we have mentioned earlier in this chapter it is here that the most significant scope for automation exists. Indeed, to perform many of the data processing functions now commonly used in monitoring, considerable computational effort may be required. Processing may be done on or off-line and this choice will   predominantly depend upon whether the monitoring system is one which operates on a continuous basis, or not. Usually continuous monitors must process data on line. Other units, for example signal analysers, are more likely to be used on an occasional basis as an off-line technique. The distinction cannot be clearly drawn.

In order to appreciate fully the requirements of the processing task it is helpful to consider in greater detail some of the more important techniques used in the monitoring process.

Perhaps the simplest form of processing is one in which the magnitude of the raw incoming signal is examined on a regular basis, as a function of time. In fact this is essentially the basis of all visual inspection techniques, which involve the active collection of data by personnel. The processing, in such cases, may consist of a comparison of the current record with the previous value or with some preset, or predetermined, value. This process is simple to automate, even when many hundreds of inputs are being monitored. The processor is simply required to associate the incoming reading with a particular item of plant. If the incoming data is required to be trended, so that in the event of an atypical event the lead up to it can be examined, then a data storage medium is essential. Magnetic tape or disc storage is the commonest method, although bubble memory storage can also be used. Semiconductor memory may also be appropriate provided it can be protected against instrument power failure, by the use of a battery back up system. It is very easy to accumulate exceedingly large volumes of data, when monitoring many inputs, so it is desirable to have automatic refresh of the data storage such that after a given period of time the data storage elements either transfer their contents to a bulk storage media, or are over-written by the incoming data stream.

When a plant malfunction is detected a common practice is to annunciate the event, and discontinue data storage on that channel. In this way the diary of events leading up to the malfunction is preserved for subsequent examination, if required.

3.5.2 Other Common Processing Techniques

In recent years several techniques for data reduction and manipulation have found great favour in the monitoring activity. Pre-eminent amongst them are the techniques known generically as spectral analysis, correlation, and time-averaging. The growth of application of these methods has closely followed the development of computing hardware and software, and whilst systems incorporating these forms of analyses used to be extremely expensive, much more modestly priced instruments of great power and flexibility are now available. The Hewlett-Packard dynamic signal analyser, model 3561/A, shown in Figure 3.13, is an example of this new range of monitoring tools. They provide the operator with the ability to analyse one or two data channels in great detail, on a more or less continuous basis. They may also be used for periodic inspection of many data channels, but they demand significant skill levels from the operator. See reference [3.7].

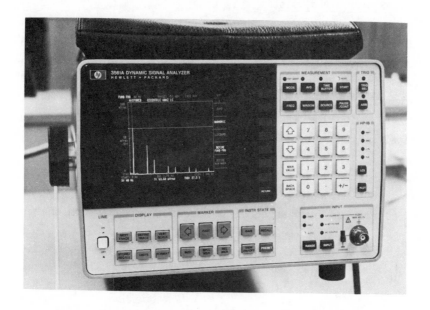

Figure 3.13 : A modern dynamic signal analyser
(Courtesy of Hewlett-Packard)

It is fair to say that the development of such techniques and instruments for monitoring has been largely in response to the demands of operators running turbo-machinery, and other mechanical plant. Vibration measurement is the main weapon when monitoring such plant, and a vast literature has developed in this area over the past two decades. The measurement of vibration is also now routinely used with electrical machines, and we shall discuss this in detail in Chapter 6.

It is impossible in a text this size to treat the analytical techniques mentioned above in any great detail, nor indeed would it be desirable, but because of their importance to modern monitoring systems we shall outline the most important features of them.

3.5.3 Spectral Analysis

Spectral analysis is the name given to describe methods that transform time signals into the frequency domain. The spectral representation of a time signal is therefore a collection of components in the frequency domain. The transformation is achieved using the techniques of Fourier analysis whereby any periodic signal, of period T,

$$g(t) = g(t + T) \qquad \qquad \text{... (3.8)}$$

is represented by the equally spaced frequency components,

$$G(f_k) = \frac{1}{T} \int_{-T/2}^{T/2} g(t)\, e^{-j 2\pi f_k t}\, dt \qquad \qquad \text{... (3.9)}$$

where k is the kth harmonic of the fundamental f. The time signal is obtained from the inverse relationship,

$$g(t) = \sum_{k=-\infty}^{\infty} G(f_k)\, e^{j 2\pi f_k t} \qquad \qquad \text{... (3.10)}$$

We see that a continuous periodic time function can therefore be represented as a discrete series in the frequency domain. The advantages are immediately apparent; our continuous input can be approximately represented to the required accuracy by a finite (and often small) set of numbers. This compacts the data significantly, and allows trends to be more easily recognised.

Because it is often necessary to digitize transducer signals for onward transmission to the processing unit of a monitoring system, the incoming data is also sampled in time. That is, it is represented as a series of discrete values at equally spaced instants in time, in a similar fashion to the frequency domain representation of a continuous time signal. Under these conditions the equivalent statement to equation (3.9) becomes,

$$G(f_k) = \frac{1}{N} \sum_{n=0}^{n-1} g(t_n) \, e^{-j2\pi nk/N} \qquad \qquad \ldots (3.11)$$

and the corresponding inverse transform is,

$$g(t_n) = \sum_{k=0}^{N-1} G(f_k) \, e^{j2\pi nk/N} \qquad \qquad \ldots (3.12)$$

In these expressions we see that the frequency is effectively sampled at the discrete frequencies f_k whilst the time signal is sampled at instants t_n. We therefore have a means of representing a discrete time function by a set of discrete values in the frequency domain. This transformation is known as the Discrete Fourier Transform (DFT). In practice this transformation is carried out using the Fast Fourier Transform (FFT) technique, which is an extremely efficient way of achieving a DFT.

The use of signals in the frequency domain shall be considered further in Chapter 6, when dealing with vibration monitoring techniques. Further details can be found in references [3.8] and [3.9].

3.5.4 Correlation Functions

Correlation between two signals, in the time domain, is a process mathematically very similar to that of convolution. The auto-correlation function provides a measure of the similarity between a waveform and a displaced version of itself, whilst the cross correlation function refers to two different time functions.

The auto correlation function of a function f(t) can be written as,

$$R_{ff}(\tau) = \int_{-\infty}^{\infty} f(t-\tau)\, f(t)\,dt \qquad \dots (3.13)$$

The function f(t-τ) is a delayed version of f(t), by a time τ. Essentially the process may be thought of as one signal searching through another to find similarities.

If $R_{ff}(\tau)$ is plotted against τ then the result is a correlogram. This will exhibit peaks when similarities between the two waveforms are detected.

Figure 3.14 illustrates the principle. The time signals are shown in Figure 3.14 (a) and (b), and the resulting correlogram in (c). It is apparent that signals exhibiting a periodicity, which may be difficult to extract from a background of noise, can be identified using this technique.

The cross-correlation function of two signals f(t) and h(t) may be written as,

$$R_{fh}(\tau) = \int_{-\infty}^{\infty} f(t-\tau)\, h(t)\, dt \qquad\qquad \dots (3.14)$$

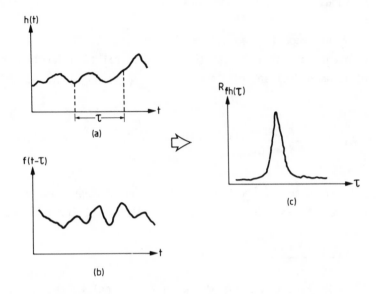

Figure 3.14 : The use of correlation functions

The similarity between correlation and convolution is now clearly seen. For example the convolution of the two time functions f(t) and h(t) would be expressed as,

$$g(t) = \int_{-\infty}^{\infty} f(t-\tau)\, h(\tau)\, d\tau \qquad\qquad \dots (3.15)$$

The only difference is that one of the time functions is effectively reversed.

Like the auto-correlation function, the cross correlation function can also be used to recover both the amplitude and phase of signals lost in a noise background.

If we redefine equations (3.13) and (3.14) in a slightly different way, that is let the cross correlation function between two signals f(t) and h(t) be,

$$R_{fh}(\tau) = \lim_{T\to\infty} \frac{1}{T} \int_0^T f(t-\tau)\, h(t)\, dt \qquad \ldots (3.16)$$

it is easy to see how the correlation process can be realised physically. Figure 3.15 illustrates the activity schematically.

3.5.5 Signal Averaging

In Figure 3.15, the need for signal averaging is noted during the practical computation of correlation functions. The averaging technique has found considerable favour in its own right for the detection of defects in gear boxes and rolling element bearings. It achieves this by simply averaging a large number of samples, taken successively from the same transducer, with each sample carefully timed to the same period. With rotating plant the rotational period of the element under inspection is usually chosen. In this way noise generated elsewhere in the system is effectively smoothed out, and the signals due to defects which exhibit a cyclic pattern over the chosen period, enhanced.

Averaging can be implemented using one of the many transient signal capture techniques. For example if it is necessary to take the average of 1000 records, say, then each record must be captured then stored for a simple average to be obtained on a point-by-point basis. This is obviously an inefficient technique since it requires large amounts of digital storage. It is possible to reduce this requirement significantly by defining the average of a quantity as, see reference [3.7],

$$\bar{x}_n = \bar{x}_{n-1} + \frac{x_n - \bar{x}_{n-1}}{n} \qquad \cdots (3.17)$$

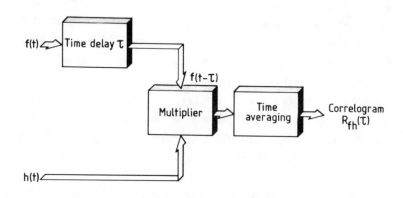

Figure 3.15 : Implementing the measurement of
correlograms

In equation (3.17) n is the record number, x_n is the value for n^{th} record, and $\bar{x}_n$ and $\bar{x}_{n-1}$ are the average values for the nth and $(n-1)^{th}$ records respectively. Using this technique it can be seen that only two records need be stored at any given time, yet the true average is always calculable. The corresponding saving of digital memory is obvious, but it has been gained at the expense of requiring more rapid processing hardware, particularly if the period of each record is short. This problem is not always significant, however, since it is nearly always possible to choose records with suitable gaps between them. It is of paramount importance to ensure that each record is properly synchronised, however.

3.5.6 Output Presentation

The processing unit is the link between the data-acquisition task and the interpretive phase of the monitoring activity. It is therefore imperative that the results achieved here are presented unambiguously and in the simplest form possible, compatible with the complexity of the information to be output. It is preferable that the operator is able to interrogate the processing system, for in this way the volume and detail of output remain under his control. The initial response of the system should be simple, but should also provide visual display via a vdu, for example, and have the facility to provide hard copy. Most modern signal analysers now give many levels of output processing using both hardware and software keyed functions.

If the interpretation of the processed results is to be carried out automatically then a secure and standard data link between the processor and the diagnostic unit must be provided. Again, most proprietary analysers have IEEE or RS232 output ports.

3.6 THE DIAGNOSTIC TASK

It is the diagnostic task that closes the loop in the monitoring activity by virtue of the fact that decisions made here should profoundly influence operational and maintenance strategy, as shown in Figure 1.3 in Chapter 1. Perhaps it is because of the fact that decisions made at this stage inevitably commit capital that the commonest form of diagnostic processor is still the man. It is true to say that expert systems derived from knowledge bases are now beginning to appear in diagnostic procedures. One need look no further than the medical practitioner's clinic to see this, but the final arbiter remains the man. There are many arguments that can be advanced as to why this should be, or whether it is desirable or not. The proponents of totally automated diagnostics will argue that the complexity of decision-making, and the sheer volume of data to be examined and processed, in an effective monitoring exercise in a large industrial organisation, is beyond the capabilities of man. It is not the intellectual problem that defeats us, but the size of the problem.

Those against leaving the machines to watch over and control the machines argue with some strength that it is not the size of the problem that defeats the computer, but the heuristic elements of the interpretation of results which only man is capable of doing.

The current status is therefore one in which a limited degree of totally automated monitoring is possible on simple systems, but the capabilities of the current generation of induction type algorithms are much too limited when more complicated systems are being monitored. The trend, however, is definitely towards more computer aided diagnostics, including heuristic programming techniques, but many fundamental questions relating to reliability, safety, and cost-effectiveness must be answered before total computer monitoring is achieved.

The aircraft industry has shown that it is possible to automate monitoring and operational systems to a very high degree of sophistication, and to do so cost-effectively. There still remains the doubt, in some minds, that if computers are best at monitoring and man most adaptable at flying the aircraft, why does the pilot watch the instruments whilst the computer flies the plane. The notion of the electronic shell is one which deserves attention, in this regard. The aim is to provide a shell around the operator that allows him significant operational freedom, but whenever he moves to the unsafe/uneconomic/unreliable boundaries of the shell, the system "pushes" him back in.

It is likely that fully automated monitoring will move in this direction in the future.

CHAPTER 4

Electrical Techniques for Monitoring

4.1 INTRODUCTION

In Chapter 1 it was explained that protective relays were the earliest electrical techniques for monitoring motors, but the technology of these devices is dated and their purpose is almost exclusively to detect gross perturbations in the electrical quantities at the terminals of the machine.

Within the machine there is a magnetic flux and electric field which varies, circumferentially in the airgap, periodically in space and, for an a.c. machine, periodically with time. Under ideal conditions these magnetic flux and electric field waveforms will be symmetrical but electrical defects in the machine will distort them. Rotor defects could be detected by electrical sensors fixed to the rotor, and stator defects could be detected by electrical sensors fixed to the rotor. Defects on either rotor or stator disrupt the radial and circumferential patterns of flux in the machine causing changes which can be detected outside the machine. These internal magnetic and electric field distortions will also alter the machine terminal quantities, the voltage and current, which can be measured to give an indication of machine condition.

In the following sections we describe a number of these new techniques.

4.2   GENERATOR AND MOTOR STATOR FAULTS

4.2.1   On-line Discharge Detection

General

A study of the failure mechanisms in Chapter 2 shows that an
early indicator of many electrical faults in machine stators is
an increase in electrical discharge activity. This activity can
also be related to the remanent life of the insulation system.
The accurate detection of discharge activity would therefore give
a valuable early warning of failure and could provide information
about the remaining life of the insulation.

Electrical discharges are transitory disturbances which radiate
electromagnetic, acoustic and thermal energy from the discharge
site. That radiation will cause perturbations to the waveforms
of the voltage and current both within the machine and at the
machine terminals and there are various electrical techniques for
detecting these perturbations on-line.

USA Method

The earliest work, summarised by Emery et al [4.1], describes a
technique developed by Westinghouse in the USA to detect the
presence, on-line, of subconductor arcing in the stator windings
of large steam turbine generators, by measuring perturbations in
the winding current. Arcing activity produces very wide-band
electromagnetic energy, some of which propagates into the neutral
connection of the star-connected winding. Emery uses a ferrite-
cored current transformer (CT) wrapped around the neutral cable
to couple to this activity, which he detects using a quasi-peak,
radio interference field intensity (RIFI) meter, as shown in
Figure 4.1. The neutral cable was chosen as a good measurement
location because it is a low potential with respect to ground and

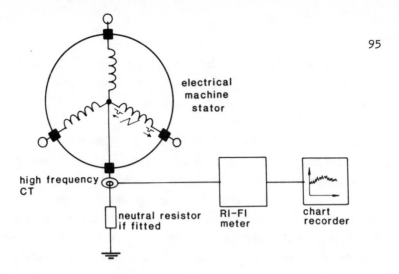

Figure 4.1 : Detection of discharge activity in a generator
Taken from Emery et al. [4.1]
© IEEE (1981)

because arcing at any location in the generator causes RF current
to flow into the neutral lead. The CT has a frequency response
from 30 Hz to 30 MHz and the RIFI meter has a narrow bandwidth of
~ 10 kHz centred at about 1 MHz. The centre frequency is tuned
to match resonances in the winding which the arcing activity
excites; the RIFI meter effectively measures the average peak
energy received by the instrument. The CT and RIFI meters are
proprietary items and a simple monitoring system can be assembled
using these components. Westinghouse have also developed a
specialised RF monitor based on this technique which is fully
described in [4.1]. The monitor interfaces with a remote panel
located in the machine control room and provides a permanent
record of arcing activity, with alarm indications to the operator
when a severe increase occurs. Emery has shown in [4.1], with
further details in [4.2], positive proof of the detection, not
only of subconductor arcing, but also of sparking in other parts
of steam-turbine-driven generators. However, the change in
signal level when arcing occurs, from the RIFI meter tuned to

1 MHz, is not dramatic. An increase of less than 50% of the unfaulted indication is typical and this makes the setting of alarm levels for such a monitor difficult.

Timperley [4.3] has used this technique and applied it not only to steam turbine generators but also to hydroelectric machines in the American Electric Power Service. He appears to have used wider bandwidth quasi-peak RIFI instruments connected to the neutral CT because he analyses the received signal in both the frequency and time domains. Using the technique he has shown some evidence of the detection of slot discharge activity on hydroelectric machines and other forms of unexpected corona activity.

Earth loop transient monitor

Wilson et al.[4.4], in the UK, have devised a similar technique to that of Emery as a cheap method of detecting discharge activity on-line in a wide range of high voltage plant. Initially it was applied to a relatively small, identifiable section of insulation, such as a stop joint in an oil-insulated ehv cable, and was known as an earth loop transient monitor. It has since been applied to the insulation of generator and motor stator windings. It uses a Rogowski coil, wrapped around the neutral cable of the machine winding, and the detector is a narrow band instrument which measures the average peak energy received by the instrument as shown in Figure 4.2. The Rogowski coil is an air-cored solenoidal search coil which is closed on itself round a current carrying conductor. The manufacture of these coils has been patented in the U.K. [4.5] and they are called Rogowski coils to distinguish them from their ancestor, the Chattock potentiometer which is not normally used for current measurements. The frequency response of the Rogowski coil is relatively wide but the detector has a narrow bandwidth of ∼ 15 kHz centred at a value determined by the application and the

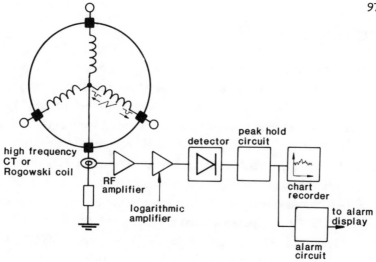

Figure 4.2   Continuous monitor of discharge activity using
an Earth Loop Transient Monitor.
Taken from Wilson et al.[4.4]

background radio noise, but usually for a generator or motor
winding this would be 1 MHz. The monitor is calibrated in
picocoulombs and is provided with alarm circuits, so that when
the discharge level exceeds a warning threshold an alarm signal
can be transmitted to the plant control room. Wilson has
explained that when applying this technique to a distributed
insulation system, such as a machine winding, care must be taken
in the calibration, because energy may be propagated to the
instrument from a number of different discharge sites in the
insulation simultaneously. Wilson has provided in [4.6] a
theoretical model for the manner in which energy, in the
frequency band detected by the instrument, is propagated from the
discharge site in to the winding neutral and he has shown how
this propagation depends critically on the configuration of the
winding and the size of the stator core.

Canadian Method

An alternative technique, where perturbations in voltage waveforms are detected at the machine terminals, has been described by Kurtz et al [4.7] and applied primarily to hydroelectric alternators in Canada. Connection to the winding is made through coupling capacitors connected to the line terminals of the machine as shown in Figure 4.3. Discharge pulses are coupled through these capacitors to a specialised pulse height analyser, which characterises, in the time-domain, the waveforms of the pulses. The bandwidth of the electronics in the analyser is 80 MHz and this is considered sufficient to capture partial discharge pulses with rise times of the order of 1 ns to 10 ns. In the early days of this technique the coupling capacitors had to be connected to the machine during an outage but in a later publication Kurtz et al. [4.8] describe how

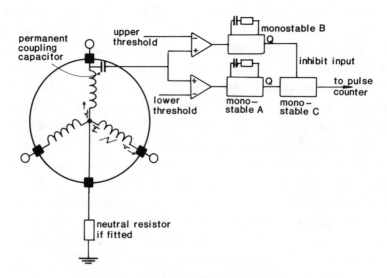

Figure 4.3 : Detection of discharge activity using a
coupling capacitor.
Taken from Kurtz et al.[4.8]

capacitative couplers can be permanently built into the phase rings of the machine so that the measurements can be made without service interruptions. In addition these permanent couplers are also intended to ensure that discharge activity from the electrical supply system, to which the machine is connected, is rejected. However, the pulse height analysis of discharges by this method is still carried out at intervals during the life of the machine rather than continuously on-line. Kurtz has not shown how the electromagnetic energy from a discharge site is propagated through the winding to the coupling capacitors but he has shown empirically that the method is capable of detecting slot discharges and the steady deterioration of winding insulation with time.

Wide band RF techniques

All the techniques described above operate at relatively low frequencies (1-80 MHz) and detect the electromagnetic energy propagated along the winding to the neutral or line end connections.

In any healthy machine there will be a background of corona and partial discharge activity which will vary from machine to machine and also varies with time. Malik et al.[4.9] have shown that damaging discharge pulses, such as serious partial discharges, sparking or arcing, have faster rise-times than the background corona and partial discharge activity and they therefore produce a much higher frequency of electromagnetic energy (350 MHz). In [4.9] it is shown that if this energy is detected, at as high a frequency as possible, the ratio of damaging discharge signals to background activity is increased. Frequencies of electromagnetic energy >4 MHz propagate from the discharge site by radiation from the winding, not by propagation along the winding as in the case with the lower frequency techniques. This radiation can be detected by a radio frequency

(RF) aerial located either inside the enclosure of the machine or outside, close to an aperture in it. In [4.9] a monitor for detecting damaging discharge activity is described based on this idea, as is shown in Figure 4.4. It receives the energy from the aerial and amplifies it before detection. The monitor contains a band-pass filter which is tuned above the cut-off frequency of background activity (~ 350 MHz), avoiding any inteference from nearby radio or radar stations, to the part of the spectrum which is of interest. The output of the monitor is a chart record which shows the instants in time at which the energy due to damaging discharge activity exceeded a threshold value. This threshold can be set according to the level of background activity in the machine.

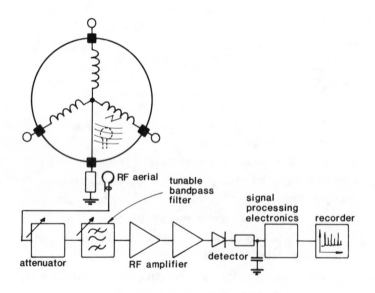

Figure 4.4 : Detection of damaging discharge activity
using RF energy.
Taken from Malik et al.[4.9]

The monitor has been used successfully on large operational steam-turbine-driven generators, where the aerial is relatively easy to fit outside the casing by mounting it close to the neutral point connection. The instrument has positively identified proven subconductor arcing and has been shown to detect other forms of damaging discharge activity. Its advantage over the other techniques is that by detecting at higher frequencies the signal-to-noise ratio of damaging activity to background is much larger and this makes it much easier to determine alarm settings for the instrument, as is shown in Figure 4.5. On the other hand the received signal cannot be related directly to discharge magnitudes in picocoulombs and all timing information about the discharge is lost.

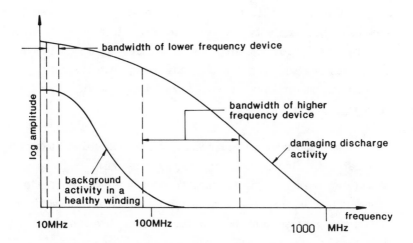

Figure 4.5 : Radio frequency energy from background
and damaging discharge activity

Detection problems

The lower frequency work (1 MHz-80 MHz), involving propagation along a homogeneous conductor, suggests that a discharge site can be located by timing the arrival of discharge pulses received at a number of different sensors. However, this has not yet been demonstrated and the existence of reflections at each discontinuity in the winding will make the identification of pulses at the terminals extremely difficult.

At higher frequencies (100 MHz-1 GHz) a discharge site could be located using a directional aerial. But at the frequencies involved the dimensions of such an aerial (diameter from 0.6 m to 6 m) would be impracticably large and in any case the complex gas space structure will cause reflections and local resonances which will disrupt location.

It must be made clear that there is less value in being able to detect discharge activity if, when the machine is taken out of service, that activity is impossible to locate. It would be preferable to allow damaging discharge activity to continue until it had reached such a pitch that the damage was observable. This highlights the problem of what constitutes a significant level discharge activity.

The low frequency devices produce an output which is generally calibrated in picocoulombs of discharge because the response can be related directly to the amplitude of a discharge calibration pulse. This allows the user to see the measured activity in discharge terms so that he can decide what level of activity he considers to be damaging. The problem is that when the discharge activities of a number of identical windings are measured off-line there is a considerable variation in the background activity due to changes in environmental conditions near the windings, small changes in the homogeneity of the insulation and so on. In other words one cannot say with any certainty what the background discharge activity for a winding should be, and in any case this activity will vary naturally with time regardless of whether any damaging activity is taking place.

It has been described how at higher frequencies the ratio of damaging activity to background will be much higher than at low frequencies. So the higher frequency technique has the potential for providing a clearer indication when damaging discharge activity occurs. But the problem still remains to determine what level of activity constitutes damage serious enough to be locatable. Further work is obviously needed and should include gaining experience of these techniques on operational machines.

4.2.2 Brushgear Fault Detection

Brushgear, in those machines which use it, requires a steady maintenance commitment if good performance with the minimum of sparking is to be maintained. Poor performance can be detected by measuring brush or brush-holder temperature but a more direct method would be to detect the radio frequency energy generated by sparking, as described by Michiguchi et al.[4.10]. They use a wide bandwidth dipole antenna connected to an RF amplifier with a bandwidth from 10-100 MHz. The output of the amplifier is rectified and the following processing electronics effectively measure the area under any pulses of RF power which enter the monitor as a result of sparking activity at the brushes. The monitor thereby produces a chart record showing the average area of sparking pulse and Michiguchi relates this to a Spark Number indicating an intensity of sparking. Maintenance staff make use of this indication to decide when brushes should be changed.

4.2.4 Rotor Mounted Search Coils

We have not found any techniques reported for detecting stator faults by search coils mounted upon the rotor. No doubt the usefulness of this technique is affected by the need to mount expensive instrument slip rings on the rotor and its effectiveness will be limited by the reliability of the measurement brushgear, which, as will be described in the section on shaft voltages, is notoriously poor.

4.3 GENERATOR ROTOR FAULTS

4.3.1 General

The rotors of large turbogenerators are particularly highly rated because of the large mechanical and electrical stresses placed upon them, in particular the high centrifugal forces on the winding and the relatively high temperatures attained in the winding insulation. Consequently that part of the machine is particularly prone to faults which, as Chapter 2 has said, tend to develop over a long period of time. The rotor is also relatively inaccessible both for obtaining signals during running and for removal for repair if a fault is detected. These facts, taken together with the high value of turbogenerator plant, have meant that monitoring techniques for generator rotors have been developed to a high degree of sophistication. Some of the techniques described below are also applicable to smaller output machines, but have yet to become fully accepted.

4.3.2 Earth Leakage Faults On-Line

A single earth leakage fault on a generator rotor winding is not serious in itself, because it cannot cause any damage as the earth leakage current is limited to leakage resistance of the excitation supply. However, if two well-separated earth faults occur then large currents can flow, leading to significant damage to the winding, its insulation and the rotor forging. The normal procedure for detecting earth faults in a large generator rotor is to apply a d.c. bias voltage to the rotor winding and to monitor the current flowing to the rotor body via an alarm relay, see Warrington [4.11] and Figure 4.6(a). If such an alarm occurs many utilities would consider that the machine should be shut-down so that the rotor can be investigated. However, operational pressures are often such that this is not possible, and it is necessary to continue running the unit. The next step then is to monitor the earth leakage current and manually trip the unit if there is any further increase, indicative of a second earth fault.

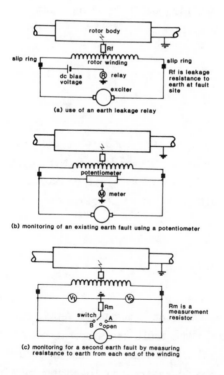

Figure 4.6 : Detecting rotor earth faults
based on Hargis et al.[4.12]

An alternative method is to use a potentiometer feeding to earth via a sensitive galvanometer making a bridge circuit, as shown in Figure 4.6(b). As the earth fault location alters or a second fault occurs the bridge unbalances and an indication occurs on the meter. The problem is that the second earth fault may arise close to the location of the first fault and the resultant change in earth leakage current may not be particularly large.

A more sensitive indicator of the onset of a second earth fault is the resistance of the winding to earth, measured from either terminal. Hargis et al.[4.12] have described such a technique using two voltmeters, V_1 and V_2, as shown in Figure 4.6(c). When the switch is open the fault position, K, defined as the fractional position up the winding from the negative slip ring, can be calcualted:-

$$K = \frac{V_1}{V_1 + V_2} \qquad \ldots (4.1)$$

When the switch is closed to A the voltages V_1 and V_2 will change by an amount depending on the fault resistance, R_f, and the current flowing through the fault, I_f, so that now the apparent fault position K' is given by:-

$$K' = \frac{V_1'}{V_1' + V_2'} \qquad \ldots (4.2)$$

From the apparent change in fault position $\Delta K = K'-K$ the voltage across the fault resistance can be calculated and finally the fault resistance itself. This procedure can be repeated, by connecting the voltmeters to the other terminal of the winding, by closing the switch to B. The choice of terminal connection is governed by the initial fault position, the object being to optimise the measurement of the fault resistance, R_f. Hargis et al.[4.12] have implemented this scheme using a microprocessor-based unit which makes the measurement at each terminal of the winding at approximately one second intervals, processes the results and presents information for operating staff as well as initiating relay indications if necessary.

4.3.2 Turn-to-Turn Faults-on-Line

Air-gap search coils

Turn-to-turn faults in a generator rotor winding may lead to local overheating and eventually to rotor earth faults. In addition, the shorting of turns causes unequal heating of the rotor leading to bending and an unbalanced pull, which together cause increased vibration as described by Rosenberg [4.13] and Khudabashev [4.14]. Such faults can be detected off-line by the method of recurrent surge oscillography, described in section 4.3.3, but a way of detecting them on-line was first described by Albright [4.15] using a stationary search coil fitted in the air gap of the machine. The search coil, of diameter less than the tooth-width of the rotor, is fixed to the stator usually in the airgap, and detects either the radial or circumferential component of magnetic flux. Examples of two types of air gap search coil installation are shown in Figure 4.7. Figure 4.8 shows typical waveforms obtained from a radial search coil in a two-pole generator operating on load.

A normal two-pole rotor will have an even number of winding slots and will produce a flux wave in the air gap as follows:-

$$b_{normal} = \Sigma_n B_n \sin n\omega t + \Sigma_m B_m \sin m\omega t \qquad \qquad \text{... (4.3)}$$
$$n = 1,3,5... \qquad m \text{ even}$$

normal mmf wave   normal tooth ripple

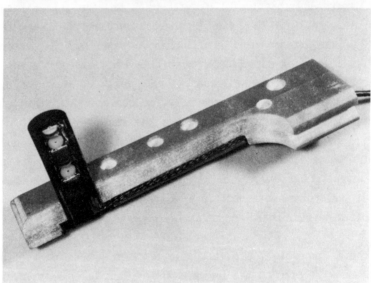

Figure 4.7 : Photographs of two typical search coil
installations in large generators
(Courtesy of NEI Parsons Ltd.)

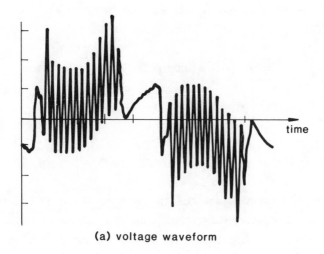

(a) voltage waveform

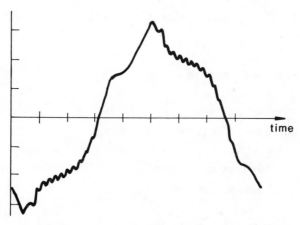

(b) flux waveform obtained by integrating (a)

Figure 4.8 : Typical voltage and flux waveforms obtained from
a generator air gap search coil
[Taken from Conolly et al.[4.16]]

And the search coil due to mmf voltage waveform will be:

$$e_{normal} = k \frac{db}{dt} = \Sigma \, kn\omega \, B_n \cos n\omega t + \Sigma \, km\omega \, B_m \cos m\omega t$$

$$\ldots (4.4)$$

$$n = 1,3,5 \ldots \qquad\qquad m \text{ even}$$

$$\text{normal mmf wave} \qquad\qquad \text{normal tooth ripple}$$

where k is the effective search coil area.

The n odd harmonics are due to the wave shape of the mmf wave in the air gap and are dependent upon the spread of winding slots over the rotor pole pitch. The m even harmonics are due to the rotor tooth ripple which is present in the voltage waveform. When a shorted turn occurs two things happen. First it disturbs the mmf distribution, causing low-order even harmonics or asymmetry in the flux and search coil voltage waveforms. Second it disrupts the nth order slot ripple harmonics. This is shown as follows:-

$$e_{fault} = \Sigma \, kn\omega \, B_n \cos n\omega t$$

$$n = 1,3,5$$

normal mmf wave

$$+ \, \Sigma \, k\ell\omega \, B_\ell \cos \ell\omega t$$

$$\ell = 2,4,6 \ldots \text{dependent on fault location}$$

fault asymmetric mmf

$$+ \, \Sigma \, km\omega \, B_n \cos m\omega t$$

$$m \text{ even}$$

normal tooth ripple

$$+ \, \Sigma \, (m+p)\omega \, Bn \cos(m+p)\omega t$$

$$p = \pm 1. \, \pm 3$$

fault tooth ripple $\qquad\qquad\qquad \ldots (4.5)$

The heights of the corresponding peaks and troughs in the ripple will change so that the search coil voltage will no longer be symmetrical about zero.

In principle the changes in the heights of the peaks and troughs can be used to determine the number and location of any shorted turns and this is what Albright did in his original paper. He identified faults by measuring the peak heights of the ripple from polaroid photographs of the oscilloscope waveform, recorded under open and short circuit test conditions. He did not consider that waveforms obtained with the generator on-load could provide the sensitivity required to detect shorted turns. Since that time a considerable number of large steam turbine-driven generators have been fitted with air-gap search coils and a great deal more experience has been obtained of detecting shorted turns. The detection techniques have therefore been refined to deal not only with the different types and locations of search coils but also to detect shorted turns under both off-load and on-load conditions.

The techniques are described by Conolly et al. [4.16] and consist first of an on-line monitor which is continuously connected to the search coil and gives an initial indication of the development of an interturn fault. Secondly more detailed analysis techniques can then be used on the search coil waveforms, off-line, to positively identify and locate the faults.

The on-line monitor measures the sum of the first four even harmonics of the search coil waveform. The purpose is to identify any asymmetry in the mmf waveform caused by shorted turns. The monitor produces an analogue signal on a chart recorder and the monitor can be adjusted so that any increase above a preset level gives an alarm which should be used to initiate the more detailed analysis.

112

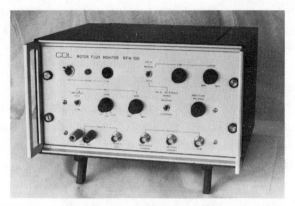

Figure 4.9 : Continuous monitor for use on an air
gap search coil
(Courtesy Convex Designs Ltd.)

The setting of that preset level depends upon the generator itself, its history and the type of search coil fitted. Again one is faced with the problems of determining background levels.

Byars [4.17] has described an alternative on-line monitor where the output voltage waveform is added to a delayed version of itself. The delay is half a cycle, thus nulling all the signals except that component which is asymmetric. An instrument to do this is commercially available as shown in Figure 4.9.

The more detailed analysis described in [4.16] requires that the waveform is collected on a digital storage oscilloscope and the digitised components of the waveform stored on a floppy disc. The waveform may initially be analysed on site, using appli-cations programs within the storage oscilloscope, or the floppy disc can be returned to base where it can be analysed fully on a laboratory-based computer system. The three main methods of analysis yield the following:-

(i) the difference between the search coil voltage waveform and a delayed version of itself, using the technique of Byars [4.17];

(ii) the amplitude of the increments in the tooth ripple in the search coil voltage waveform, using the method of Albright [4.15];

(iii) the flux waveform by integrating the search coil voltage waveform.

Before these can be done the waveform is Fourier analysed into its real and imaginary components. Conolly et al.[4.16] have shown that the waveform obtained from a search coil at one radial position in the air gap can be modified to predict the waveform if the coil were at another position closer to the rotor. This is particularly helpful for coils fitted close to the stator surface, where the rotor tooth ripple may be very small. It also allows results from different sizes and designs of machines to be compared on a common basis. The difference waveform can be calulated from the digitised components of the search coil voltage and this waveform can be plotted out to show the presence of a fault as shown in Figure 4.10.

The incremental voltages are calculated by measuring the voltage height between the peaks and troughs of each tooth ripple associated with each pole of the winding and the heights are measured on the side of the ripple furthest from the pole face. These incremental voltages can be plotted out as a histogram over the rotor surface together with a histogram of the differences between the voltages over one pole and the next as shown in Figure 4.11.

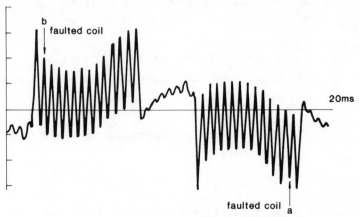

(a) search coil waveform close to rotor surface
predicted from measured search coil waveform

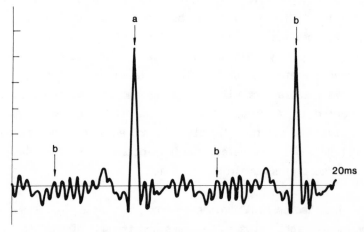

(b) difference waveform obtained by delaying half a cycle
and adding figure (a) above

Figure 4.10 : Effect of delaying and adding the waveform
from a search coil fitted to a faulty machine using the method of Byars [4.17]

The flux waveform is found by integrating the voltage waveform. Distortions of the flux waveform can be brought to light either by direct inspection or by carrying out the difference procedure described above for the search coil waveform.

Computer simulations and the practical experience of measuring search coil voltage waveforms suggest that the magnitude of the asymmetry in the search coil waveform produced by a fault depends upon the load as well as the location and number of shorted terms. This is because the degree of saturation affects the magnitude of the rotor tooth ripple, which varies with load and with position around the rotor circumference. In the absence of saturation the asymmetric component would be expected to be proportional to rotor current. However, magnetic saturation level to the shorted turn has a significant effect, so that for some loads and locations of shorted turn, the magnitude of the asymmetry actually decreases with increasing rotor current. Research is continuing on the best way to allow for this effect.

Circulating current measurement

An alternative way of monitoring for shorted turns, which is still under development, uses the stator winding itself as the search coil. The principle of this technique, first suggested by Kryukhin [4.18], has been developed and fitted to a number of generators in the UK; see Muhlhaus et al. [4.19]. This technique makes use of the fact that in large two-pole generators, each phase of the stator winding consists of two half-phase windings in parallel. Any asymmetry in the rotor mmf will induce counter-mmf currents in the stator winding with a twice funda-mental frequency, which will circulate between the half-phases. The presence of shorted turns is detected by measuring those even harmonic currents. The size of the currents depends upon the severity of the shorted turns, the coupling between rotor and

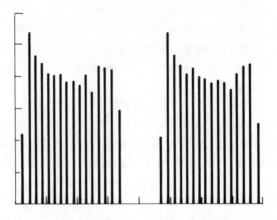

(a) incremental voltages obtained from figure 4.10a

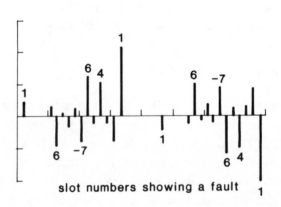

slot numbers showing a fault

(b) differences in incremental voltages between poles
obtained from figure (a) above

Figure 4.11 : Method of incremental voltages
proposed by Albright [4.15]
Taken from Conolly et al [4.16]

stator and the impedance of the stator winding to the currents. The approach has also been suggested by Buckley [4.20].

It can be shown that the emf, e, induced across a stator half-phase winding, due to a single shorted turn, spanning an angle, 2β, on a two pole rotor is given by:-

$$e = \frac{4\mu_0\omega}{\pi Cg} \ NI \ RL \ \sum_{n=1}^{\infty} \frac{1}{n} k_{wn} \ \sin(n\beta) \ \sin n\omega t \qquad \dots (4.6)$$

where   I   is the ampere-turns of the short
       ω is the rotational frequency
       N   is the number of stator turns in series per half phase
       R   is the mean radius of the air gap
       L   is the active length of the rotor
       C   is the Carter factor to account for slotting
       g   is the width of the air gap
      ν is the half angle subtended by the shorted turn
       n   is the harmonic number
     k_{wn} is the stator winding factor for the nth harmonic.

The emf induced in the opposite half-phase winding, on the same phase, will be of the same form but the term $\sin n\omega t$ will be replaced by one of the form $\sin(n\omega t - n\pi)$. The odd harmonics of the emfs in the two half-phases will therefore be of the same sign and so when the half-phases are connected in parallel they will aid one another, forming the terminal voltage due to that shorted turn. The even harmonics will be of opposite sign and so will drive circulating currents between the half phases. The currents are flowing in the stator winding, rotating at the same speed as the rotor, effectively counteracting the rotor shorted turn. The second harmonic circulating currents which flow in the stator, i_{2C}, can be related to the second harmonic emf, e_2, induced by the shorted turn, providing the second harmonic impedance, X_2, of the winding is known. Now the impedance to 2nd harmonic currents is given by:-

$$X_2 = X_{m2} + X_{\ell 2} \qquad \qquad \ldots (4.7)$$

where X_{m2} is the second harmonic magnetising reactance
$X_{\ell 2}$ is the second harmonic leakage reactance.

For a typical large machine,[4.19] gives a formula for X_{m2} and shows that $X_2 = 0.516$ pu. Therefore for a single shorted turn spanning an angle of 2β on the rotor the second harmonic current circulating in the stator winding is given by:-

$$i_{2C} \simeq e_2/0.516 \qquad \qquad \ldots (4.8)$$

The currents are detected using air-cored Rogowski coils wrapped around the winding and a diagram of an on-line monitor for doing this is shown in Figure 4.12.

An advantage of this new technique, when compared to air gap search coils, is that the current transducers can be installed without the need to remove the rotor from the generator. For many generators the half-phase windings are joined within the cooling pressure casing in a fairly restricted space which requires special arrangements to gain access. But on some machines the half-phase windings are joined outside the casing, so fitting of the Rogowski coils becomes even simpler. Care must of course be taken to provide appropriate high voltage insulation and electrostatic screening between the Rogowski coil and the

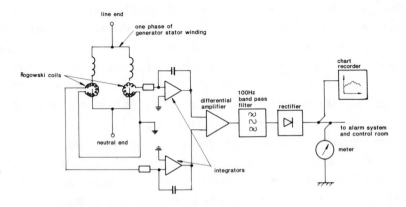

Figure 4.12 : Continuous monitor for use on circulating
current Rogowski coils

conductor. A disadvantage of the circulating current method,
however, is that it does not readily give information on the
location of a shorted turn, whereas the air gap search coil
method does.

Neither the air gap search coil nor Rogowski coil method appears
to have been applied to multi-pole hydro-type generators or even
4-pole turbine-type machines. No doubt applications will evolve
as operational circumstances demand them.

4.3.3   Turn-to-Turn And Earth Leakage Faults Off-Line

Surge techniques have been used for many years by transformer
manufacturers for locating defects in windings. More recently
turbogenerator manufacturers have used similar techniques for
pin-pointing faults in their rotor windings, as a quality control
check immediately after a rotor has ben assembled. Grant [4.21]
has shown that such a technique can be used to detect both earth
leakage and turn-to-turn faults on generators during their

service lives. He used a mercury-wetted contact relay to develop recurrent, rapid rise-time (c 20 ns) surges which he injected into the winding between the slip-ring and the earthed body of the rotor. Figure 4.13(a) shows this recurrent surge generator, which is switched on and off at a frequency of 50 Hz, while Figure 4.13(b) shows the connection of the generator to the rotor winding. The winding approximates to a simple transmission line where the propagation is dominated by the geometry and insulation of the winding conductor in the rotor slot. Mutual coupling between turns of the winding will cause dispersion but this effect has been found to be small in solid steel rotors. When the surge is injected at one end it has a magnitude determined by the source impedance, R, of the recurrent surge generator and the surge impedance of the winding, Z_o. The surge propagates to the far end of the winding in a time, t, determined by the length and propagation velocity of the winding. The surge is reflected at the far end, its magnitude determined by the reflection coefficient, k. For a winding with the far end open-circuited, k = +1 and with it short-circuited k = -1. The reflected surge returns to the source and if the source impedance equals the surge impedance of the winding (k = 0 at source), it is absorbed without further reflection. This is shown in Figure 4.14(a).

When an insulation defect to earth, or a turn-to-turn fault, is encountered, this reflection pattern will be disrupted and may be observed on the oscilloscope. The pattern on the oscilloscope is known as a recurrent surge oscillograph (RSO) and this has become the name of the technique. The rise time of the surge will affect the method's sensitivity and must be less than the propagation time of the surge-front through a single winding turn for sharp reflection to occur.

Figure 4.14(b) shows results obtained from the practical application of this method. The source impedance R was adjusted to be equal to the winding surge impedance and a surge of between

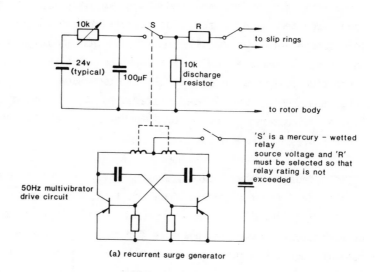

(a) recurrent surge generator

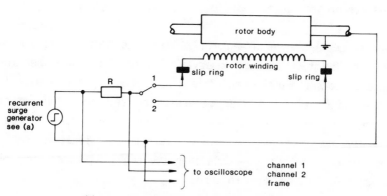

(b) connection of the recurrent surge generator to a rotor winding

Figure 4.13 : Arrangements for obtaining a recurrent surge
oscillograph from a rotor winding
Taken from Grant [4.21]

10 and 100 volts was applied with a rise time of 20 ns. The surge was injected into each end of the winding, with the far-end open-circuited, and two reflection traces were obtained as shown in Figure 4.14(b) (i and ii), either of which should be compared to the ideal response of Figure 4.14(a)(i). The results show the distortion of the trace as a result of dispersion and the lack of surge sharpness. Faults are indicated by superimposing the two traces and observing any deviations between them, as shown in Figures 4.14(b) (ii and iii).

Earth faults may be located, approximately, by taking the ratio of the times for reflections from the fault and from the end of the winding. Similarly the electrical length of the winding can be estimated by measuring the time for the surge to make a single pass through the winding. This can be done by short circuiting the far-end of the winding to obtain a trace like Figure 4.14(a)(ii). Any shortening of the length indicates that shorted turns are present in the winding.

The surge impedance of a rotor winding lies between 20 and 30 ohms. A deviation becomes observable on the RSO trace when the imepdance to earth of the fault is a significantly small multiple of the surge impedance. In general, the technique can detect faults with impedances to earth of less than 500-600 ohms. Similarly the technique can detect a turn-to-turn fault which has a resistance significantly less than the surge impedance, say of the order of 10 ohms down to zero.

To carry out RSO measurements the generator must be isolated, the field de-energised and the exciter connection disconnected. It is known that many rotor faults are affected by both gravitational and centrifugal forces upon the conductors during rotation, so it is common to carry out the tests stationary, at barring and at speed for comparison purposes. The test has now been applied by many utilities as a routine technique for

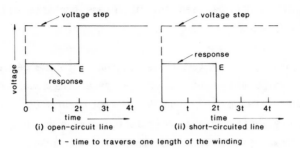

t – time to traverse one length of the winding
E – start of reflection from winding end

(a) the ideal response of a rotor winding to injected surges

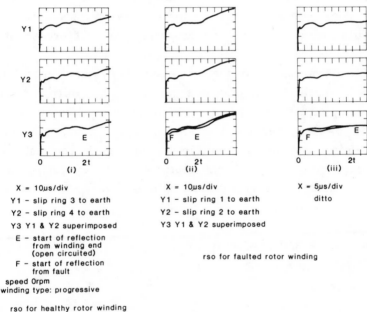

X = 10μs/div
Y1 – slip ring 3 to earth
Y2 – slip ring 4 to earth
Y3 Y1 & Y2 superimposed
E – start of reflection
from winding end
(open circuited)
F – start of reflection
from fault
speed 0rpm
winding type: progressive

rso for healthy rotor winding

X = 10μs/div
Y1 – slip ring 1 to earth
Y2 – slip ring 2 to earth
Y3 Y1 & Y2 superimposed

rso for faulted rotor winding

X = 5μs/div
ditto

(b) typical responses for rotor windings

Figure 4.14 : Ideal and typical practical recurrent surge
oscillographs obtained from generator rotor
windings
Taken from Grant [4.21]

124

assessing the operational state of machine windings, although it is clear it cannot be used for brushless machines without the rotor being stationary.

The advantages of the technique are that with the oscillographs it provides a permanent record of the state of a rotor throughout its service life and it can detect both earth and interturn faults before their resistance falls to a value where large fault currents flow. Experience has shown that the deterioration of a winding can be assessed by a comparison between oscillographs obtained from the same rotor. It is not possible, however, to make comparisons between oscillographs from different rotors, even if they are of the same design, because of the effects on the surge propagation of quite small variations between the insulation and rotor body properties of different rotors.

The disadvantages are that it detects faults of high resistance and is unable to differentiate between faults which are opera-tionally significant and those which are not. Also it cannot be used on-line, testing the winding under truly operational mechanical and thermal conditions. This is in contrast to the effectiveness of the air gap search coil or circulating current method which can provide on-line information.

4.4   MOTOR ROTOR FAULTS

4.4.1   General

The rotors of other electrical machines can be highly stressed, though perhaps not to the same degree as turbogenerators. In particular large induction motors with either squirrel cage or wound rotors have problems, as the experience of Barker and Hodge [4.22] shows. A number of both electrical and mechanical techniques have developed to monitor these problems. This section deals with the electrical techniques.

4.4.2 Air-Gap Search Coils

The work on air-gap search coils, described in Section 4.3.2, was all used on turbogenerators but there is no reason why the method should not be successfully applied to smaller machines. Indeed Kamerbeek [4.23] has successfully used the method experimentally on small induction motors but for measuring torque rather than machine defects. A very recent paper by Seinsch [4.36] has applied this technique to induction motors using a distributed coil on the stator.

4.4.3 Stator Current Monitoring

Although the technique of using a stator search coil has not been widely used, it is possible to use the stator winding itself as a search coil, in a somewhat similar way to the method described for generators in Section 4.3.3. Any rotor defect in an induction motor will cause a characteristic swing in the supply ammeter reading, which maintenance staff have come to recognise as indicating that trouble is on its way. Careful measurement of the stator current will therefore enable such a defect to be monitored.

The current drawn by an ideal motor should have a single component of supply frequency. Changes in load will modulate the amplitude of the current to produce sidebands. Defects in the rotor circuit will generate a sideband below the supply frequency and displaced from it by twice the slip frequency. This effect is described by Hargis et al.[4.24]. A motor winding with p pole pairs and supply frequency ω produces an mmf wave, m_1, at mechanical angle θ containing odd harmonics only. Consider the fundamental:-

$$m_1 = N_1 I_1 \sin(\omega t - p\theta) \qquad \cdots (4.9)$$

where N_1 is the number of stator turns

I_1 is the stator current.

The phase angle, ϕ, on the rotor is given by:-

$$\phi = \theta - \omega_r t \qquad \cdots (4.10)$$

where ω_r is the rotational speed of the rotor.

So that a two-pole rotor sees the mmf:-

$$m_1 = N_1 I_1 \sin((\omega - \omega_r)t - \phi) \qquad \cdots (4.11)$$

which rotates forward with respect to the rotor at the slip speed. Under normal circumstances the rotor carries induced currents, m_2, to balance the stator mmf:-

$$m_2 = N_2 I_2 \sin((\omega - \omega_r)t - \phi) \qquad \cdots (4.12)$$

If the rotor has a defect, such as a broken bar, the mmf due to the rotor current is modulated by $\sin 2\phi$ so that

$$m_2 = N_2 I_2 \sin((\omega - \omega_r)t - \phi)\sin 2\phi \qquad \cdots (4.13)$$

therefore

$$m_2 = \frac{N_2 I_2}{2} \{\cos((\omega - \omega_r)t - 3\phi) - \cos((\omega - \omega_r)t + \phi)\}$$
$$\cdots (4.14)$$

Referring this mmf to the stator, as the counter to equation (4.11), using equation 4.10 gives:-

$$m_1 = \frac{N_2 I_2}{2} \{\cos(\omega + 2\omega_r)t - 3\theta) - \cos(\omega - 2\omega_r)t + \theta)\}$$
$$\dots (4.15)$$

which if we use the fractional slip $s = (\omega - \omega_r)/\omega$ for a two-pole machine gives:-

$$m_1 = \frac{N_2 I_2}{2} \{\cos((3 - 2s)\omega t - 3\theta) - \cos((1 - 2s)\omega t - \theta)\}$$
$$\dots (4.16)$$

Now the first component of mmf, because it contains $3\omega t$ and 3ϕ, induces zero sequence emfs in the three phase stator winding which gives rise to no current contribution from the supply. The second component of mmf, however, induces a proper 3-phase set of currents at the normal supply frequency but contains a component, or sideband, $2s\omega$ below that frequency.

It is effectively a twice slip frequency modulation of the supply current which is seen as the swing on the ammeter reading. Such a cyclic variation in the current reacts back on the rotor to produce a torque variation at twice slip frequency which, if the rotor does not have an infinitely high inertia, gives rise to a twice slip frequency speed variation described in reference [4.24], that can also be used for fault detection as described in Chapter 5. This speed effect reduces the lower sideband, $\omega(1-2s)$, current swing and produces an upper side band at $\omega(1+2s)$, enhanced by modulation of the third harmonic flux in the stator. The ratio of the lower sideband amplitude to the main supply frequency component gives a straightforward indication of the extent of rotor damage, as described by Jufer et al.[4.25].

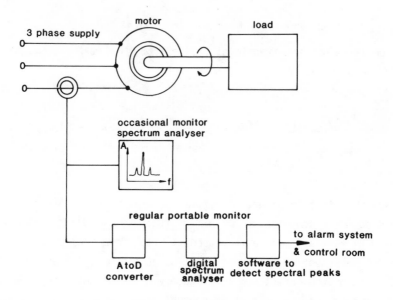

Figure 4.15 : Detecting sidebands in the supply current
of an induction motor
(Courtesy of CEGB)

The supply current may be monitored very easily, without interfering with the machine, simply by fitting a clip-on current transformer around the supply cable to the motor, see Figure 4.15. The normal procedure is to use a high resolution spectrum analyser connected directly to the CT, or to use it on a tape recording of the current signal, surveys of the supply current being taken at regular intervals during the machine life, or when a fault is suspected. Figure 4.16(a) and (b) shows the current spectra from two identical machines, the first of which had a rotor defect corresponding to three fractured cage bars. The lower sideband due to the mmf modulation can clearly be distinguished from the supply frequency. To prevent any ambiguity a separate measurement of motor speed, obtained from the rotor slot ripple component of the supply current, should be required but this has rarely proved necessary on operational motors.

Because the current measuring technique looks into the motor from the terminals it is also possible to see beyond the electrical circuits and detect defects in the mechanical load train, such as worn gear teeth, which the motor is driving. Figure 4.16(c) shows the current spectrum from a motor which had no (1-2s) component, indicating rotor damage, but was driving a load with a damaged gear-box. This was shown by the spectral components at 42, 47, 53 and 58 Hz.

The spectrum analyser technique requires a relatively skilled operator to carry out a survey of a machine and it cannot be considered as continuous monitoring. The normal practice would be to carry out a survey whenever ammeter swings indicate that a problem is imminent. Where motors of high value are at risk,more frequent or continuous monitoring may be necessary. For this purpose a digital instrument has been devised, as shown in Figure 4.15, which samples the current waveform, carries out a Fourier transform and analyses the sidebands.

The technique has also been applied to small motors as described by Steele et al.[4.26]. Notelet et al.[4.27] have also used a similar technique, not for rotor circuit defects, but for detecting rotor eccentricity as a consequence of bearing wear. They have derived expressions for the pulsation of the supply current as a result of variations in the mutual inductance of the stator windings due to the rotor eccentricity and have confirmed these expressions by experiment. A diagram of the continuous

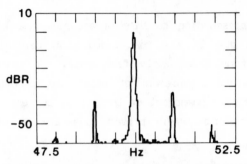

(a) motor with three contiguous broken bars

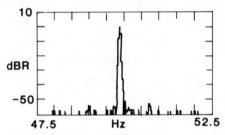

(b) identical motor to (a) with no broken bars

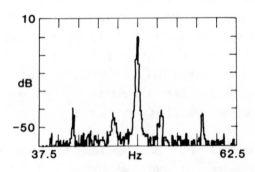

(c) motor driving through a damaged gearbox

Figure 4.16 : Supply current spectra from induction motors
with and without faults
Taken from Hargis et al.[4.24]

monitor they propose for detecting these supply current variations is shown in Figure 4.17 but it is not clear how the
threshold levels for detection in that instrument are determined.

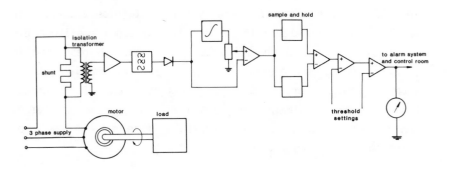

Figure 4.17 : Continuous monitor for detecting eccentricity
in the rotor of a motor
Taken from Notelet et al.[4.27]

4.4.4 Rotor Current Monitoring

The rotor circuits of wound rotor motors are usually poorly
protected in most installations. Defects in brazed joints and
slip-ring connections have sometimes caused severe damage because
they have not been detected promptly. Overheating of rotors can
also be caused by current imbalance in the external resistors or
circuits connected to the slip rings. The low frequency of these
currents makes measurements with conventional current transformers inaccurate. Faults of these types were some of the

reasons which encouraged the development of a proprietary leakage flux technique which is described later in Section 4.5, see Rickson [4.28]. However, low frequency currents can be measured accurately by Rogowski coils. These have been used to monitor the rotor resistance currents in variable speed wound rotor motors as shown in Figure 4.18 and the technique has been described briefly by Ellison et al.[4.29]. The signals from the Rogowski coils are integrated to give a voltage proportional to rotor current. These signals are summed to give the mean current in all three phases of the rotor and are compared to the individual phase currents. Processing electronics then detects whether severe unbalance is present and provides amplitude and alarm signals to the control room. The approach described in [4.29] is based upon a protection philosophy, in that indications from the monitor are used to trip the machine. In practice, however, the instrument has been used to provide monitoring indications which assist in determining when motors should be taken out of service for repair.

4.5   GENERATOR AND MOTOR FAULTS - COMPREHENSIVE ELECTRICAL
       METHODS

4.5.1 General

The reader should be able to see, both from the introduction to this chapter and from the methods which have been described, that electrical techniques have much in common. There would seem to be some advantage in devising a single electrical technique which is capable of detecting all electrical faults, whether they are on the rotor or stator. Various methods have been proposed and we describe here two of them which detect defects by measuring the effect they have on the machine flux at the rotor shaft.

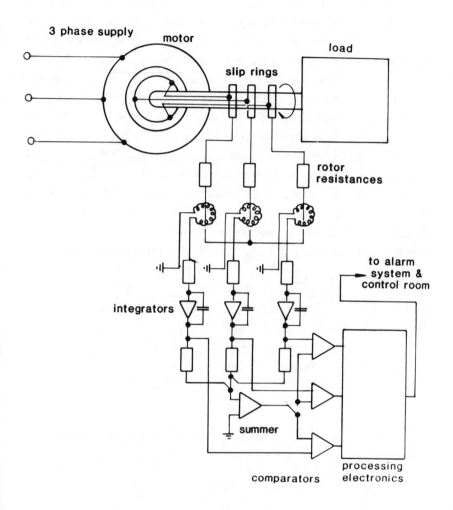

Figure 4.18 : Continuous monitor of rotor current in a wound
rotor induction motor
Taken from Ellison et al.[4.29]

4.5.2 Shaft Voltages and Currents

Many electrical power utilities have attempted to monitor the voltages induced along the shafts of electrical machines in the hope that they may be a useful indicator of machine core or winding degradation and also because on large machines they can give rise to large shaft currents which are damaging to bearings. Figure 4.19 shows how a voltage can be induced between contacts sliding on a rotating machine shaft whenever fluxes in the machine are distorted, either from the normal radial and circumferential pattern, or from the normal axial pattern. These sliding contacts may be the result of rubs in defective bearings or seals or could be brushes placed to detect flux distortion. The brushes would normally be placed at either end of the machine to embrace the complete shaft flux circuit. If a defect, such as a rotor winding shorted turn, produces a rotating distortion of

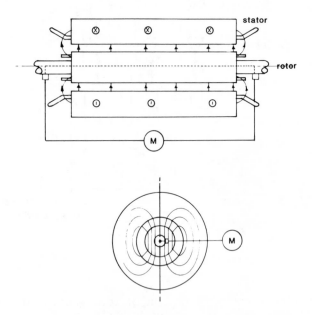

Figure 4.19 : The production of shaft voltages due to asymmetries in the magnetic field of the machine

the field in the radial and circumferential plane, then an a.c. or pulsating shaft voltage results. If a defect produces a distortion of the field in the axial direction then this gives rise in effect to a homopolar flux which produces a d.c. shaft voltage. In steam-turbine driven machines, shaft voltages can also be produced by electrostatic action, where the impingement of water droplets on turbine blades charges the shaft. Verma et al.[4.30] have given a very full report on the mechanisms for the production of shaft voltages and currents and the faults they may indicate. Methods of monitoring shaft voltages usually include making a.c. and d.c. measurements of the voltage and sometimes analysing the harmonic content of the waveform. Verma has proposed a comprehensive shaft voltage monitor in [4.30].

Our experience, however, is that shaft voltage has not proved to be a useful parameter for continuous monitoring. The voltage is difficult to measure continuously because of the unreliability of shaft brushes, particularly when they are carrying only a small measurement current. In addition, it has been shown by the authors' colleagues that any damage to the core and winding would need to be substantial before a significant variation in shaft voltage occurred.

This should not detract, however, from the normal regular maintenance procedure of measuring shaft voltages at bearing pedestals, from time-to-time, in order to check the pedestal insulation and to confirm that there is no tendency for large shaft currents to flow.

4.5.3 Shaft Fluxes

Shaft flux, or more generally axial leakage flux, occurs in all electrical machines. It is produced because no machine can be constructed perfectly symmetrically. There will always be, for example, slight differences in the reluctance of magnetic circuits due to building tolerances, core plate anisotropy, and plate thickness variation. This asymmetry is reflected in the impedances presented by the various phase groups, or coils in the machine stator, and will cause slight variations in the currents flowing in the coils. This, together with small differences in the electrical properties of the conductor, and variations in the physical disposition of the conduction in both the active length and end regions of machines, will give rise to a net difference between the currents flowing in one section of the end winding when compared with the corresponding section diametrically opposite. The imbalance leads naturally to a net axial flux component. A similar argument can be applied to the rotor circuits; hence one can expect axial flux even in machines that are in 'perfect health'.

It is a simple extension of the above to consider what happens when certain fault conditions arise in a machine. Faults, such as winding short circuits, voltage imbalance, and broken rotor bars, represent severe disruptions to the internal symmetry of the machine. It is logical to conclude, therefore, that the effect on the production of axial flux will be readily observable. Any gross change of magnetic circuit conditions, such as the formation of an eccentric air gap due to bearing wear, will, by the same token, be reflected with a corresponding change in axial leakage flux.

The purpose of axial flux monitoring is therefore to translate observed difference in the nature of the axial leakage flux into an indication of fault condition. The production of such fluxes in squirrel cage rotor induction machines has been studied by Jordan et al.[4.31, 4.32] with particular emphasis on the changes occurring due to static eccentricity. Erlicki et al.[4.33] have shown that it is possible to detect the loss of a supply phase through axial flux monitoring and Rickson developed a monitoring device [4.28]. More discrimination between variety of fault conditions can be achieved by carefully processing the axial flux signal as described by Penman et al. [4.34, 4.35]. The technique relies upon examining the changes in the spectral components of the axial flux. These components arise as described below.

Since the fluxes are produced by winding currents, the frequency of these flux components must be related to the frequencies of the currents. Rotor currents are also induced by the airgap flux, so the net airgap flux will be modified as a result. While the rotor is at rest the airgap field results solely from the currents flowing in the stator; hence only the time harmonics present in the line currents will appear in the axial flux. Once the rotor moves, however, it does so with an angular speed of $(1-s)\omega/p$ with respect to the stator, where p is the number of pole pairs in the machine. The airgap flux components will consequently be frequency shifted. For example, in the normal three-phase stator winding, the airgap field, b, produced has the form:

$$b^S = B_1\cos(\omega t - p\theta) + B_5\cos(\omega t + 5p\theta) - B_7\cos(\omega t - 7p\theta) + B_{11}\cos(\omega t + 11p\theta)$$

$$\ldots (4.17)$$

We can transform this expression into a frame of reference moving with the rotor by considering Figure 4.20, which shows the relationships between a fixed point in the stator and a fixed point on the rotor:

$$\phi = \theta - \omega_r t \qquad\qquad \ldots (4.10)$$

138

but for a machine with p pole pairs:

$$\phi = \theta - (1-s) \omega t / p \qquad \qquad \dots (4.18)$$

Using the expressions it can be shown that the nth term of the airgap field in the stator frame is:

$$b_n{}^S = B_n \cos[(1 \pm n(1-s))\omega t \pm np\phi] \qquad \dots (4.19)$$

and the corresponding expression to 4.17, in the rotor frame, is:

$$b^r = B_1 \cos(\omega t - p\phi) + B_5 \cos[(6-5s)\omega t + 5p\phi]$$

$$- B_7 \cos[(7s-6)\omega t - 7p\phi] \qquad \dots (4.20)$$

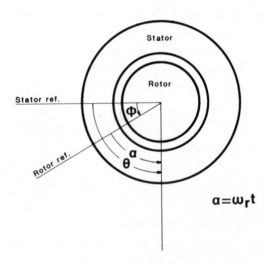

Figure 4.20 : Rotor and stator frames of reference

Obviously the first airgap harmonic produces currents at 5 times the supply frequency; the fifth produces time frequencies of (6-5s)ω and so on.

It is now apparent that the axial flux spectrum will be rich in harmonics, even in a well-constructed, healthy machine. Moreover, because fault conditions such as shorted turns, loss of phase, eccentricity and so on cause changes in the space harmonic distributions in the airgap, such conditions will be accompanied by a corresponding change in the time harmonic spectrum of axial flux. Furthermore by effectively using the stator winding as a search coil to detect rotor faults, and the rotor winding to detect stator faults, it is possible to gain insight into the harmonic changes to be expected for a given fault condition.

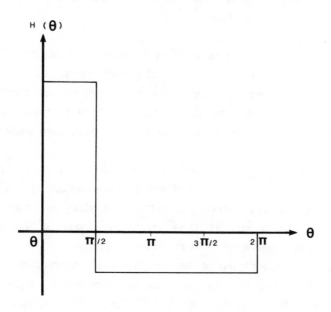

Figure 4.21 : Mmf due to a single fully pitched coil

Let us follow a typical fault condition through the diagnostic procedure. If we assume that an interturn short circuit exists in the stator winding then this condition results in a single pulse of mmf, similar to that shown in Figure 4.21. The components of airgap field generated by this distribution are:

$$b^S = \sum_n B_n \cos(\omega t \pm n\theta) \qquad \qquad \dots (4.21)$$
$$n = 1,2,3,5$$

and the nth component in the rotor frame will therefore be:

$$b_n^r = B_n \cos[(1 \pm \frac{n}{p}(1-s))\omega t \pm n\phi] \qquad \dots (4.22)$$

These harmonics will flow in the rotor circuits, and because there are necessarily asymmetries in the rotor magnetic and electric circuits, they will appear as additional components in the spectrum of axial flux.

Figure 4.22 illustrates results taken from a small four-pole squirrel cage induction machine using the technique. In these cases only the spectral components up to 500 Hz are shown, but faults such as interturn short circuits, broken rotor bars, or negative phase sequence in the supply lines have been identified.

The axial flux monitoring technique is still embryonic but essentially it requires the collection of an axial flux signal, using a search coil wound concentrically with the shaft of a machine. This signal is then spectrally analysed and on the basis of the appearance of certain harmonic groups a decision is made as to the condition of the machine. The attractions of the method are that it is completely non-invasive and a single sensor can be used for a variety of fault types. It is, however, a complicated technique requiring specialised equipment, and is relatively untested.

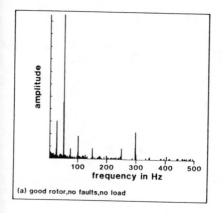

(a) good rotor,no faults,no load

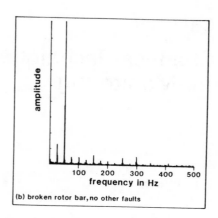

(b) broken rotor bar, no other faults

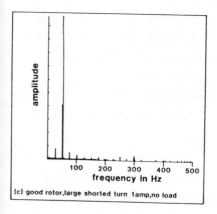

(c) good rotor,large shorted turn 1amp,no load

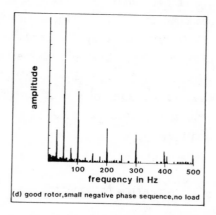

(d) good rotor,small negative phase sequence,no load

Figure 4.22 : Typical spectra taken from an axial flux search coil fitted to an experimental motor

CHAPTER 5
Chemical Techniques
for Monitoring

5.1 INTRODUCTION

Both insulating materials and lubricating oils are complex organic materials which, when they are degraded by heat or electrical action, produce a very large number of chemical products in the gas, liquid and solid states. Lubrication oils also carry, not only the products of their own degradation, but also those from the wear of the bearings and seals they cool and lubricate. Any technique to detect degradation needs to measure the concentration of one or more of these complex products in the most appropriate state, at the most convenient location in the machine.

5.2 INSULATION DEGRADATION

What are the mechanisms by which insulation can be degraded? Well, the table in Appendix I (p.50) shows how important thermal degradation is as a failure mechanism and this is largely determined by the thermal performance of the insulation. The insulation consists in the main of organic polymers. Either natural forms such as bitumen, or, more commonly nowadays, synthetic epoxy resins. The thermal degradation of these materials is a complex process. However, as the temperature of the insulation rises above its maximum permitted operating value, circa 160°C, volatiles used as solvents in the insulation manufacture start to be driven off as gases. Then the heavier compounds making up the resin may reach their boiling point. The gases so produced are generally the heavier hydrocarbons such as ethylene. As the temperature rises further, above 180°C, chemical decomposition of the resin components starts. A supersaturated vapour of the heavier hydrocarbon decomposition products then forms in the cooling gas close to the high temperature area of insulation. Rapid condensation of that vapour occurs as the cooling gas leaves the hot area producing condensation nuclei which continue to grow in size by further condensation until they reach a stable droplet size. These droplets, usually called particles, are of submicron size and form what would commonly be called smoke. The precise materials given off depend primarily on the insulation material being heated but also on the cooling gas of the machine. The binder material of the insulation, whether it be wood, paper, mica or glass fibre,can usually withstand much higher temperatures, but eventually, as 400 °C is reached,they start to degrade and char, releasing gases such as carbon monoxide and carbon dioxide, drawing oxygen from the cooling gas, if it is air, or from the degradation of the complex hydrocarbon in the resin. Figure 5.1 shows a piece of phenolic impregnated wood insulation from a turbogenerator, raised to progressively higher temperatures in hydrogen. Up to 300°C one can see the effects of the resin material being decomposed and driven off, but the wood binder still retained its strength. Above 400°C the binder has degraded by charring and no longer has significant mechanical strength.

Pyrolysing activity therefore gives rise to a wide range of gases, liquid droplets and even some solid particulates which together make up the smoke being driven off from the insulation.

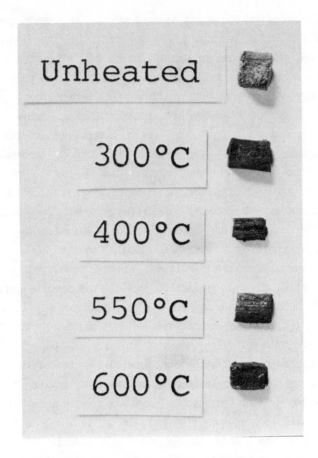

Figure 5.1 : Heating of phenolic impregnated wood
insulating material

Electrical discharge activity, within or adjacent to the insulation system, also releases chemical degradation products. The very high temperature associated with sparking breaks down the hydrocarbon compounds in the insulation to form acetylene. It also breaks down the oxygen in the cooling gas, if it is air, to give ozone. Furthermore, continuous discharge activity gradually carbonises and erodes the insulating material to produce, on a smaller scale, the degradation products which result from more widespread overheating.

5.3 FACTORS WHICH AFFECT DETECTION

Before considering the different methods of detecting chemicals within an electrical machine it is necessary to understand the factors which affect the detectability. Consider Figure 5.2(a) which shows the machine within its enclosure. Now the rate of change of concentration of a detectable substance can be determined by the following equation:

$$\left[\begin{array}{l}\text{Rate of change of concentration}\\ \text{of detectable substance in the}\\ \text{cooling circuit of the machine}\end{array}\right] = \frac{\left[\begin{array}{l}\text{Rate of production of the}\\ \text{detectable substance -}\\ \text{Rate of its leakage out of}\\ \text{the machine}\end{array}\right]}{\text{Machine volume}}$$

$$\frac{dC}{dt} = \frac{\dot{\nu} - \frac{VC}{\tau_r}}{V} \qquad \ldots (5.1)$$

where V   is the machine volume

C   is the volumetric concentration of the substance concerned

$\dfrac{1}{\tau_r}$ is a leakage factor

$\dot{\nu}$ is the volumetric rate of production of the detectable substance.

Now obviously the leakage factor is small when leakage is low, so τ_r is effectively a residence time constant for the substance in the machine enclosure. The rate of production, ν, is related to the volume of material being overheated, and its chemical composition. This variable is in fact a function of time $\nu(t)$. So the equation can be rewritten:-

$$\frac{dC}{dt} + \frac{C}{\tau_r} = \frac{1}{V} \dot{v}(t) \qquad \ldots (5.2)$$

$$(D + \frac{1}{\tau_r})C = \frac{1}{V} v(t) \qquad \ldots (5.3)$$

The complementary function for this equation is:-

$$C = A \exp(-\frac{t}{\tau_r}) \qquad \ldots (5.4)$$

The particular integral is:-

$$C = \frac{(\dot{v} + \dot{v}_b)\tau_r}{V} \qquad \ldots (5.5)$$

where $\dot{v}(t) = \dot{v} + \dot{v}_b$,

$\dot{v}_b$ is the background rate of production of the substance,

$\dot{v}$ is a step increase in the rate of production.

When $t = 0$, $C = C_b$ the background concentration.

$$C_b = \frac{\dot{v} \, \tau_r}{V}$$

$$\therefore \ A = \frac{\dot{v}_b \, \tau_r}{V} \qquad \ldots (5.6)$$

$$\therefore \ C = \frac{\dot{v} \, \tau_r}{V} (1 - \exp(\frac{t}{\tau_r})) + \frac{\dot{v}_b \, \tau_r}{V} \qquad \ldots (5.7)$$

By studying equation 5.7 it is possible to determine how the detectable concentration depends upon the design of the machine, the nature of the overheating fault it is suffering from, and the

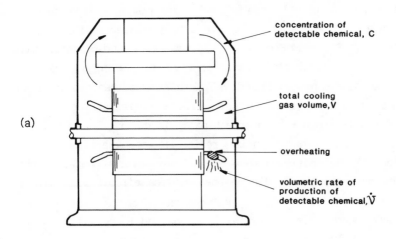

(a)

concentration of
detectable chemical, C

total cooling
gas volume, V

overheating

volumetric rate of
production of
detectable chemical, $\dot{V}$

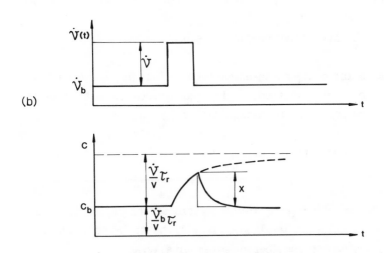

(b)

Figure 5.2 : The concentration of detectable chemicals in
coolant gas of an electrical machine

a) cross section of machine
b) response of the concentration of detectable
chemical to a step change in the rate of
production of that chemical

material involved. Figure 5.2(b) will help to explain this. A machine with a tightly sealed and pressurised cooling system, such as a turbogenerator, will have a long residence time, τ_r, of many hours. So, from Figure 5.2(b), the background concentration level of the detectable substance, C_b, will be high. On the other hand the concentration level, which can be reached after an extended period of overheating, will be correspondingly high. But if the length of the overheating incident, τ_o, is short, say a few minutes, compared to the residence time then the concentration will not build up to a significant level compared to the background. A machine with an open cooling circuit will have a short residence time, τ_r, of perhaps merely a few seconds. So the background concentration will be low and there will need to be a large volumetric production, $\dot{v}$, from an overheating incident to produce a large increase in concentration C. But the concentration level will respond rapidly to any overheating.

Detectability of overheating depends upon:-

(i) a large signal-to-noise ratio. That is, the magnitude of the indication, (X in Figure 5.2(b)), must be large compared to the background, C_b;

(ii) a long duration of indication.

The larger the signal-to-noise ratio of the indication and the longer its duration the easier it will be to detect. These two conditions can be considered mathematically:-

For i) $\dot{v} \gg \dot{v}_b$

and $X \gg \dfrac{\dot{v}_b \tau_r}{V}$

now $X = \frac{\dot{\nu}}{V} \tau_r (1-\exp(\frac{\tau_o}{\tau_r}))$

where τ_o is the duration of the overheating incident

so $(1-\exp(-\frac{\tau_o}{\tau_r})) \gg \frac{\dot{\nu}_b}{\dot{\nu}}$

$\therefore \ 1 - \frac{\dot{\nu}_b}{\dot{\nu}} \gg \exp(-\frac{\tau_o}{\tau_r})$

That is:

$\dot{\nu}$ must be $\gg \dot{\nu}_b$ and $\tau_o > \tau_r$,
or ν must be $> \dot{\nu}_b$ and $\tau_o \gg \tau_r$

For ii) $\tau_o \gg \tau_r$

The time constant of τ_o depends upon the type of fault causing the overheating, including its extent, the nature of the material being overheated and the substance being released which we are trying to detect. For example, a small intermittent shorting of turns in the rotor winding of a large turbogenerator will probably only produce heating for a few minutes, and the increase in concentration of detectable substances in that time will be small because of the long residence time, τ_r, in such a machine. But on the other hand overheating in a terminal connection or due to excessive stray losses will operate for many hours and produce a substantial indication.

The effect of the substance being detected can be considered as follows. An insulation material which is heated at a steady but relatively low temperature of say 190°C will produce a considerable amount of hydrocarbon gases over a lengthy period of time, up to 2-3 hours, until those gases are all driven off. Particulates will also be formed but these will have a short lifetime in the enclosure because of recombination and condensation, say 10-15 minutes. If the insulation is raised to higher temperatures the production of copious quantities of gases will take place over a much shorter period of time and will stop before charring commences. If the machine is air-cooled large amounts of carbon monoxide and carbon dioxide will also be produced if overheating takes place over a long period of time because production of those gases continues even during charring.

All these factors need to be taken into consideration when deciding which of the following techniques should be applied to a particular machine to detect a certain type of fault.

5.4 DETECTING INSULATION DEGRADATION

It can be concluded from Section 5.2 that insulation degradation can be monitored chemically by detecting the presence of particulate matter in the coolant gas or by detecting simple gases, like carbon monoxide and ozone, or more complex hydrocarbon gases, like ethylene and acetylene. Let us consider these approaches in turn.

5.4.1 Particulate Detection - Core Monitors

Detecting the smoke given off from degrading insulation appears the simplest and most general of all techniques since proprietary smoke detectors already exist which use an ion chamber to detect the particles in the smoke. An example is shown in Figure 5.3. As the cooling gas of the machine enters the ion chamber it is ionised by a weak radioactive source. The gas then flows through an electrode system to which a polarizing voltage is applied.

The free charges in the gas are collected on the electrode and flow through an external electrometer amplifier circuit, which produces an output voltage proportional to the ion current. When heavy smoke particles enter the chamber they too are ionised and their greater mass implies a lower mobility compared to the gas molecules, so as they enter the electrode system the ion current reduces. Therefore the smoke is detected by a reduction in the output voltage from the electrometer amplifier. Skala [5.1] describes an ion chamber specifically designed to detect the products of heated insulation and this was applied to a large turbogenerator by Carson et al.[5.2, 5.3].

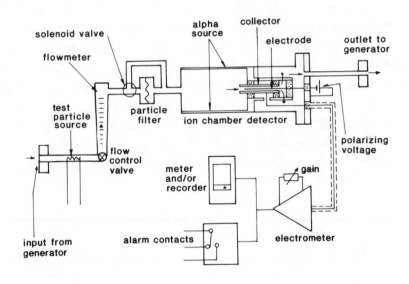

Figure 5.3 : Diagram of a basic core monitor
Taken from [5.1]

The primary impetus for this work was the need to provide early warning of core faults, which the larger sizes of turbogenerators started to experience in the mid-1960's. A core fault can involve substantial quantities of molten stator steel and, hitherto, the defect could only be detected when the melt burnt through the stator winding insulation and caused an earth fault. It was hoped that the core monitor could detect the degradation of the insulation between the steel laminations at an earlier stage in the fault. The lifetime of pyrolysed particles in the closed hydrogen cooling circuit of a large generator is 15 to 30 minutes after which time the particulates are deposited onto the exposed surfaces of the machine. So a single instance of insulation overheating should lead to a reduction of core monitor ion current for a period of time of this order. Figure 5.4 shows typical core monitor responses. When a core fault is occurring the overheating continues over a longer period and it has been shown by Carson and Wood et al.[5.3, 5.4] that the core monitor does respond to this and other forms of insulation overheating. Core monitors are now available commercially from several manufacturers in the US and UK. The sensitivity of the device depends upon the ion chamber design but experimental figures for the monitor described in [5.3] show that it will produce a response ranging from 85-95% of full scale deflection when 100 cm^2 of lamination insulation is pyrolysed, depending on the material. An area is quoted because the production of particulates is primarily a surface effect.

The device, however, does have some practical difficulties:-

(i)   the monitor output fluctuates with cooling gas pressure and temperature;

(ii) the monitor responds to oil mist which may be present in the circuit of a hydrogen-cooled machine due to faulty hydrogen seals;

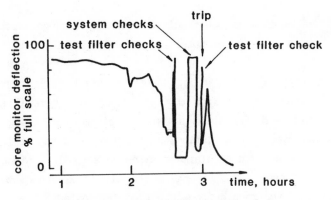

a) machine with overheating conductor bar

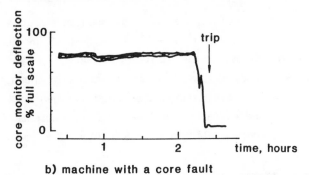

b) machine with a core fault

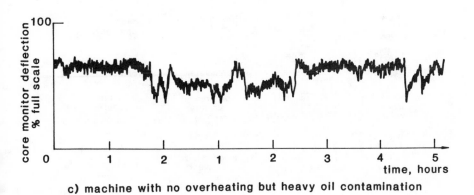

c) machine with no overheating but heavy oil contamination

Figure 5.4 : Typical core monitor responses

154

(iii) the monitor is non-specific; that is, it cannot distinguish between the materials being overheated.

Items (i) and (ii) affect the background signal from the
monitor, which any signal due to damaging overheating must
exceed. Figure 5.4(c) shows a typical core monitor trace from a
machine affected by oil mist. Item (iii) affects the attitude of
a machine operator to an alarm from the core monitor, since there
will be less confidence in the monitor if it is not known from
which part of the machine the detection originated.

A more advanced monitor, described by Wood et al.[5.4], has
been devised to overcome problems (i) and (ii) by using a
differential technique. The monitor, shown in Figure 5.5,
consists of two identical ion chambers in series in the gas flow
line with an intermediate particulate filter between them. The
monitor displays the difference between the ion currents in the
two chambers and thereby eliminates fluctuations due to pressure
and temperature.

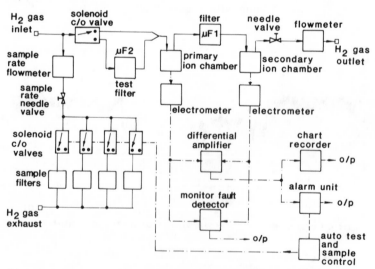

Figure 5.5 : Diagram of a differential core monitor with
heated ion chambers
(Courtesy of NEI Electronics Ltd.)

The sensitivity of a core monitor to oil-mist can be reduced if the ion chamber is kept at an elevated temperature. Lodge [5.5] has suggested that an oil mist is only produced by overheating, so that its detection may be useful. For this reason he advises against the use of heated ion chambers. However, the amount of oil in a turbogenerator casing varies widely and can be particularly high. In this case the authors and others [5.6] have found that there can be frequent false core monitor alarms, so the use of a heated ion chamber gives a significant advantage. In order to completely vaporize an oil mist it is necessary to raise the ion chamber temperature above 120°C. The monitor described in [5.4] has heated ion chambers and the authors' experience, using these set to 120°C, was that they gave an adequate protection against spurious oil mist indication. Using a heated ion chamber also means that some of the droplets produced by overheating will be vaporized, or at least reduced in size, and this must result in a consequential loss of sensitivity. However, laboratory tests can quantify this loss of sensitivity, which at 120°C has been shown to be 20%.

Early use of core monitors in the early 1970's was advocated in the US as a panacea for the early detection of major core and winding faults. Since then, however, although there have been some notable detection successes, such as those traces shown in Figures 5.4(a) and (b), there have also been false alarms, many caused by oil mist, see Figure 5.4(c).

The authors are not aware of the core monitor being used on air-cooled machines, or machines without a closed cooling circuit at all, although, apart from the short time constant of the indication from the monitor, there seems to be no reason why it should not be used for these applications. Experience has shown that the core monitor cannot usually be relied upon, on its own, to give incontrovertible evidence of an incipient fault. It is a valuable device which does detect pyrolysed insulation but its indications need to be considered alongside those of other monitoring devices. In particular the core monitor needs to be complemented by an off-line technique to chemically analyse the particulate material causing the detection, as described in the following section.

5.4.2 Particle Detection–Chemical Analysis

Many authors have advocated taking a sample of the particulate material when a core monitor indicates an alarm [5.3]. The monitor shown in Figure 5.5 is equipped with an automatic collection system to do this. In order to collect a detectable amount of particulate matter within a short time, it is necessary to have a very large gas flow-rate through the filter. This is achieved by venting the pressurised casing of the machine through the filter to atmosphere. Similar methods are used by other manufacturers. There is not such close agreement about the method of analysis however. Carson et al.[5.3] describe a method whereby the pyrolysis products are collected upon a small charge of silica gel and are then released into a gas chromatograph upon the application of strong heat. This technique is applicable only when sampling is carried out immediately upon detection of local overheating. This is because it is designed especially to collect the particulates and heaviest pyrolysis products, which are present for only a limited time in the gas, sometimes for only a few minutes.

There is also a problem with the gas chromatographic analysis of the pyrolysis products as these products contain a very large number of different organic compounds and the resultant chromatogram is difficult to interpret, Figure 5.6 gives an example. The most arduous test would be to distinguish the products of pyrolysed insulation from the overheated oil which is generally present in any electrical machine. Some authors have used a mass spectrometer in association with the gas chromatograph, to obtain

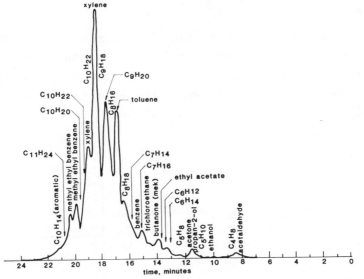

Figure 5.6 : Gas chromatogram of generator hydrogen impurities described from a Tenax GC precolumn
Taken from [5.9]

precise identification of individual compounds. But the problem then arises of how to distinguish between the very large numbers of organic compounds which are obtained and how to associate a pattern of compounds with the overheating of a particular insulation material. There is some hope that modern, computer-based pattern-recognition techniques could solve this problem, but a solution has not been reported yet.

An alternative is to reduce the amount of chemical information obtained from the pyrolysis products by using detection techniques which are less sensitive or only sensitive to pyrolysis products. One technique proposed by Ryder et al.[5.7] makes use of the fact that many organic materials fluoresce when irradiated with ultra-violet light. The resultant UV spectrum is far less complex than the chromatogram produced by the same compounds going through a gas chromatograph. Figure 5.7 gives an example, which should be compared with Figure 5.6. The filter is illuminated by a UV lamp, of a given wavelength, and the fluorescent light from the collected organic particles can be viewed with a UV spectrometer. It has been claimed that pyrolysed insulation can be clearly distinguished from oil by this technique. Further advances of the method were reported by Hogg et al. [5.8] but to date a commercial version is not available.

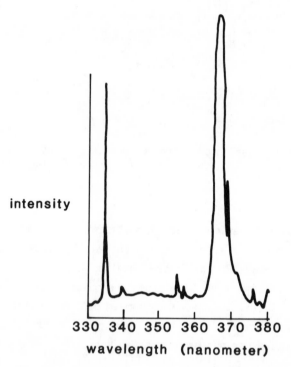

Figure 5.7 : Typical ultraviolet spectrum of hydrogen impurities
due to pyrolysed insulation
Taken from [5.7]
© IEEE (1979)

It has also been proposed that UV sensitivity could be used for the detection of the pyrolysed materials on filters using a high performance liquid chromatograph. The early chromatograms do appear promising, in that they are simple to interpret and can distinguish between the pyrolysis products from some common insulation materials.

It must be stressed that despite the various techniques described here, to the authors' knowledge there is, as yet, no definitive way to identify conclusively material collected on a core monitor filter. A way out of this difficulty is being sought by tagging components in the machine with compounds which when overheated give off material with easily identifiable chemical compositions. This technique has been used in the US by Carson et al. [5.2] but is receiving further attention in the UK (Ryder et al. [5.7, 5.8]).

5.4.3 Gas Analysis Off-Line

An alternative to detecting and analysing the particulate matter is to detect the gaseous products of pyrolysis, such as the hydrocarbon gases or carbon monoxide and carbon dioxide in the cooling gas. There may be two advantages in doing this. First from Section 5.2 it is clear that some gases are given off at lower temperatures, before particulates, so an earlier warning of overheating may be given. Second, in a closed cooling circuit, where particulates have a short lifetime of only 15-30 minutes, gaseous products will have a much longer lifetime of many days, depending upon the coolant gas leakage factor, $1/\tau_r$, so it will not be necessary to detect simply a short-term change. On the other hand, whereas the concentration of particulates will be zero in the absence of burning insulation, there will always be a small and possibly variable background concentration of gases, due to impurities in the make-up, and this will effectively determine the threshold for the detection of burning by this technique.

The gas analysis method, which has received attention for large hydrogen-cooled generators, uses a gas chromatograph and flame ionisation detector (FID) to measure the total hydrocarbon content in the hydrogen. Early work showed that most organic compounds present in the cooling gas could not be detected

160

without a concentration technique. A number have been reported but the most widely used is a pre-column method in which the impurities are absorbed on a gas chromatographic stationary phase contained in the short tube. Desorption is achieved by placing the pre-column in the carrier gas stream of a gas chromatograph and then heating rapidly. This technique has been used by Dear et al.[5.9] and is also the method used by Kelley et al.[5.10] to identify particulate matter. A similar approach is adopted by Goodman [5.11]. Kelley et al. have shown that the chromatograms produced from this sort of analysis can be used as "fingerprints" of the type of insulation involved in the overheating problem. Direct comparison of the gas chromatogram obtained from a sample with standard chromatograms can identify the insulation being overheated; see Figure 5.8. A very large number of compounds are detected and, as for particulate detection, the problem is to identify which compounds are important indicators of overheating.

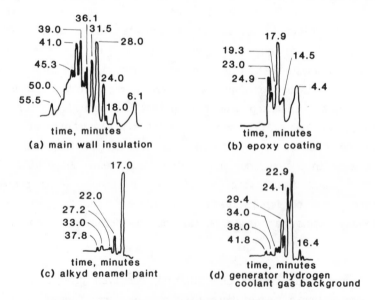

Figure 5.8 : Comparison of gas chromatograms taken from pre-column samples from hydrogen-cooled generators with overheating of various insulation components Taken from [5.10]

Again it is possible to positively identify individual compounds by gas chromatography/mass spectrometry. But is is then necessary to determine which compounds are associated with which insulation materials and this can only be done providing suitable standard samples have been overheated and accurate gas chromatograph/mass spectrometer traces obtained. This has been described by Le Gall et al.[5.12].

Pre-column samples can be taken for off-line analysis when a core monitor responds to overheating. But this would prevent any early warning advantage that gas analysis could give. More usually samples are taken from the machine at regular intervals. Some other authors have done the analysis local to the generator but if a comprehensive service, covering many machines, were to be provided this would have to be done in a central chemistry laboratory where the accuracy and quality of the analysis could be maintained. Figure 5.9 gives the results of regular analyses from a generator experiencing an overheating problem. This shows the gradual increase in concentration of organic products in the gas as the problem worsened, at which point more frequent samples were taken. The machine then came off-load for repair and when regular sampling recommenced the normal background or threshold level was found to be re-established. It can be seen from this commentary that the technique is essentially an off-line one and the warning of overheating which can be obtained is very dependent on the frequency with which samples can be taken.

Another off-line method of gas detection which has been used in modern large air-cooled machines is to measure the ozone concentration to detect the onset and progress of slot discharge erosion. Large epoxy insulated windings in an air-cooled environment experience this problem which can lead to a major insulation failure. The ozone concentration in the coolant air can be measured by taking a gas sample and using a Draeger tube.

5.4.4 Gas Analysis On-Line

The advantage of performing gas analysis continuously on-line is that, because of the long residence times of gases due to overheating in the cooling system, it may be possible to obtain earlier warning of incipient damage to the machine. The disadvantages are the inherent complexity of continuous chemical gas analysis equipment and the difficulty of translating the analysis into a single electrical signal.

Bearing in mind the experience of Kelley et al.[5.10], shown in Figure 5.9, Painter et al.[5.13] devised a continuous monitor, for application to hydrogen-cooled generators, which uses an FID to measure the total organic content of the hydrogen. This is the type of detector used in chromatography for the detection of organic species. The generator hydrogen gas is introduced into a hydrogen/air flame. The flame forms part of an electrical circuit and normally presents a very high resistance. When organic species are introduced organic ions containing carbon are formed and the resistance of the flame decreases linearly with the amount of organic compound introduced. The arrangement of the instrument is shown in Figure 5.10. The device is very sensitive and can detect increases as small as 0.2 parts per million by volume (vpm). But its usable sensitivity is reduced because of the presence of background levels of organic compounds which can be 10-50 vpm with a variability of ±20%. However, one considerable advantage of the continuous monitor over the core monitor is that it shows the trend of any increase in the products of overheating, as shown in Figure 5.11. The total organic content is measured in vpm of methane (CH_4) equivalent. However, Figure 5.11 also shows the very considerable background level against which faults need to be detected. The sensitivity of the monitor has been calculated theoretically based upon the methane equivalent content of typical insulation materials. This shows that in a large hydrogen-cooled generator the pyrolysing of

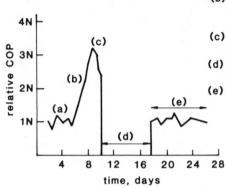

(a) 1N is equivalent to normal COP.

(b) significant increase in COP accompanied by a core monitor deflection.

(c) core monitor alarm, load reduction initiated.

(d) unit off line for inspection and maintenance.

(e) generator synchronized, COP back to normal.

Figure 5.9 : Plot of concentration of organic products during and after a generator overheating problem
Taken from [5.10]

© IEEE (1976)

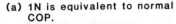

Figure 5.10 : Diagram of a continuous monitor for detecting total organic content in hydrogen cooling gas using a flame ionisation detector

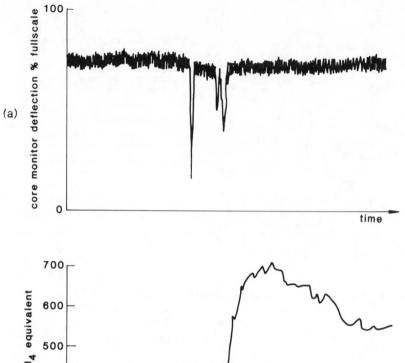

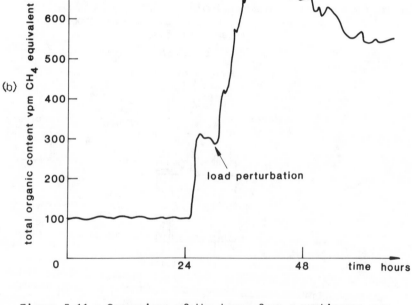

Figure 5.11 : Comparison of the trace from a continuous gas
monitor with the response of a core monitor
on a 500 MW alternator following an overheating
incident

a)   core monitor response
b)   continuous gas monitor response

24 grams of insulation would produce about 32 litres of methane equivalent hydrocarbons, which on a large hydrogen-cooled generator (500 MW) would give a concentration of about 15 vpm of methane equivalent on the FID. The amount of hydrocarbons produced depends not only on the temperature of the insulation but also on the part being overheated. The mass of insulation per unit volume in the laminated core is relatively small. Whereas on a winding if overheating takes place a very large proportion of the volume involved will be insulation and this will give a correspondingly large indication on the FID. Overheating would be considered to be serious if the rate of increase of total organics exceeded 20 vpm/h.

An alternative to the FID detector, for the detection of organic content in hydrogen, has been proposed using a commercial photoionization detector (PID) for flammable gases. The detector contains an ultraviolet lamp which ionises the gas stream as it passes through. A potential is applied across electrodes in the detector and the conductivity is measured as in the FID. The device detects the heavier hydrocarbon compounds in the gas stream and it has been shown that a fault involving overheating of about 2 grams of organic material would produce a deflection of 1 or 2 vpm on the device fitted to a large generator. Typical background levels of 7-10 vpm were measured.

On air-cooled machines an overheating incident will produce a large volume of carbon monoxide and carbon dioxide as well as the light hydrocarbon gases. Burton et al.[5.14] have described an instrument which detects overheating by measuring the carbonmonoxide concentration. The instrument contains an auxiliary pump which draws air, through tubes, from a number of motors that are being sampled to a commercial infra-red detector, as shown in Figure 5.12. The detector measures the carbon monoxide content using the principle that the vibration of the carbon monoxide molecule corresponds with a known wavelength in the infra-red region.

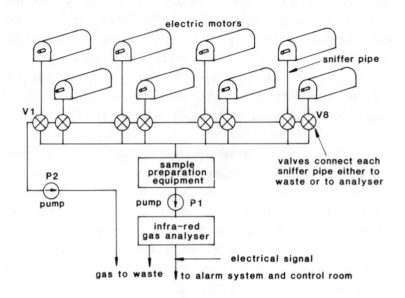

Figure 5.12 : A system for monitoring overheating in electrical
machines by detecting carbon monoxide
Taken from [5.14]

Within a totally sealed motor enclosure the air should recirculate with a long residence time, τ_r, but, because of gaps in a practical enclosure, a substantial proportion of the total volume of air is exchanged with the environment every minute. Thus any carbon monoxide in the cooling stream produced by overheating will be diluted fairly rapidly. This is in contrast with the detection problem in the sealed cooling system of a hydrogen-cooled generator. However, the infra-red analyser is capable of detecting concentration of carbon monoxide down to less than 1 vpm. Calculations have shown that 180 grams of insulation heated to 300°C will produce a 1.5 vpm rise in the concentration of carbon monoxide in the cooling air. Therefore the analyser has sufficient sensitivity to detect localised overheating on motor windings, as reference [5.14] shows. The gas scanner which operates with the instrument enables up to eight motors to be monitored sequentially. Only motors in service are sampled and the air from the motors is sampled every 2 minutes. The scanner also includes an alarm circuit which will operate if a preselected level of carbon monoxide concentration is exceeded. Experience has shown that a lower warning level of 2.5 vpm is appropriate with an alarm at 6 vpm. This alarm has not yet been used to trip the machines but rather to determine whether major repairs should take place, as [5.14] describes. The control of the scanner, auxiliary pump and alarm circuits has been implemented in a proprietary programmable logic controller which is simple and allows great flexibility in determining the way in which the motors are monitored.

5.5 LUBRICATION OIL AND BEARING DEGRADATION

The shafts of smaller electrical machines are supported by ball or roller bearings lubricated with grease and defects in such bearings could be detected by shock pulse techniques as described in Chapter 6. But high-speed machines above about 300 kW and low-speed machines above about 50 kW use oil-lubricated rolling element bearings and still larger sizes need sleeve bearings with a continuous oil supply. A number of authors including Evans and Bowen et al.[5.15, 5.16] have suggested that the continuous monitoring of that oil supply could provide early warning of incipient problems either in the oil itself or in the bearings.

The normal mode of failure of rolling element bearings is by fatigue cracking, although other wear mechanisms like fretting, scuffing and abrasion will also generate debris.

For white metalled sleeve bearings failures are not usually progressive. Debris is likely to be released in short bursts when the bearing is transiently overloaded or if an oil-film momentarily ruptures. Quite substantial damage can be tolerated whilst the bearing continues to be fed a copious supply of cooled lubricating oil. Nevertheless there are many potentially damaging situations which could be diagnosed by analysing the lubricating oil including fatigue failure or cavitation at the white metal surfaces and corrosion in the lubrication system. Any incipient bearing failure is likely to lead to local heating and degradation of the lubrication oil at the wear site.

A particular problem associated with electrical machines is the flow of currents through bearings and oil films which pit the bearing surface, producing metallic debris and degrading the lubrication oil. This sort of activity is caused by magnetically induced shaft voltages induced within the machine, whose cause and effects are summarised very thoroughly by Verma et al. [5.17]. The two approaches which could be used on the lubrication oil to detect these various types of incipient failure activity are therefore:-

(i)   the detection of oil degradation products;

(ii) the detection of bearing degradation products, or wear debris detection.

5.6 OIL DEGRADATION DETECTION

The chemical detection of oil degradation has been used most effectively for the condition monitoring of transformers, see Rogers [5.18], where the oil is used for insulating and cooling purpose and is sealed within the transformer enclosure. But in that case the mechanisms of degradation are clearly defined, being distinguished by the different temperatures reached. The technique is off-line gas-chromatograph analysis of the transformer oil, done at regular intervals during the plant life. Such rigorous analysis is necessary to distinguish between the complex products produced in the oil.

But the mechanisms involved in bearing oil degradation are not so clearly defined and the analysis that would be necessary would be more complex and less easily prescribed. However, standard off-line oil analysis procedures are available commercially but the authors do not know of any programmes that have experienced particular success with electrical machines. The typical parameters to be screened in bearing oil analysis are given in the Neale Report [5.19].

5.7   WEAR DEBRIS DETECTION

5.7.1 General

The off-line monitoring of wear debris in lubricating oils has been widely used for some time, particularly for rolling element bearings and gears, in the military and aviation fields. This has particularly made use of the ferromagnetic attraction of debris particles. In fact passive magnetic plugs fitted to lubricating oil sumps have been used, for many years, to collect ferromagnetic debris and regular inspection gives an aid to indicate when full maintenance should be carried out. But these techniques have now advanced so that on-line detection of the debris content in oil is possible. Work has also been done to extend the capabilities of on-line detection so that other debris, produced for example from white-metal bearings, can be detected. These techniques are described in the following two Sections. In reading these Sections it should be borne in mind that oil is supplied to the bearing from a closed loop lubrication system which will contain oil filtration equipment. That equipment will remove a proportion of any debris entrained so that, following a wear incident, the concentration of debris will increase and then decay away as the filters do their work. Thus the ability to detect wear debris is dependent upon volume and residence time factors similar to those which control the detectability of chemicals in cooling gas, as described in Section 5.3.

5.7.2 Ferromagnetic Techniques

The normal mode of failure of rolling element bearings is by fatigue cracking and spalling producing fragments up to a millimetre or more in size. An on-line device has been developed which can be inserted into the full-flow oil line from a bearing and count the number of ferromagnetic particles present in the oil flow, with a certain size band. The detector is based on the induction unbalance principle used in metal detectors. A pair of carefully screened coils surround the oil line and form two arms of an a.c. bridge circuit. Magnetic or conducting particles entrained in the flowing oil cause the bridge to unbalance first on one side of the null, as the particle approaches the device, and second on the other side of the null as the particle recedes. Figure 5.13 shows a section through the sensor and a system diagram. The phase of the bridge unbalance enables ferromagnetic particles to be discriminated from other conducting particles. The sensitivity of the system varies according to the shape of the particles but for approximately spherical particles the sensitivity can be adjusted to separately record the passage of particles at two size levels, small from 200 μm to 2 mm dia. and large about 2 mm dia., in an oil flow velocity of 1 to 12 m/s, that is an oil flow of up to 20 litres/s. The output is in the form of a counter reading in each of the two size ranges and the output could be made available to a data acquisition system. This

robust device is manufactured by Smiths Industries, as described
in reference [5.20], and has been widely used on jet engine
installations, where its performance in a high temperature,
pressure and vibration environment has been proved. There is no
record, however, of this device being used on an electrical
machine.

A device which can produce a greater amount of information
about ferromagnetic wear debris is the instrumented magnetic
drain plug. Conventional magnetic plugs usually consist of a
bar magnet with a pole projecting into the lubricating oil. In
an instrumented plug it is necessary to measure the change in
field strength at the magnet pole as debris is collected.
Because of the difficulties of measuring those changes a
horseshoe magnet has been adopted instead of the bar magnet. As
particles are attracted to the gap between the poles of the
magnet they decrease the field within the gap, while at the same
time increasing the total flux in the magnetic circuit. Two
differentially-connected, matched field sensors, sampling each
of these fields, can thus give additive, particle-dependent
signals, whilst cancelling out fluctuations due to temperature
and magnetic field strength. Figure 5.14 shows the arrangement
of the device which has been patented by Lloyd et al. [5.21].
The device described in [5.22] gives analogue voltages proportional to the amount of debris deposited, the rate of accumu-
lation of debris and the temperature of the oil. The device can
detect masses of ferromagnetic debris attracted to the pole
pieces ranging from 10 mg to 600 mg with a resolution of 10 mg
in an oil flow velocity of 0.1 to 0.5 m/s.

5.7.3 Other Wear Debris Detection Techniques

The ferromagnetic techniques described in the previous Section
are appropriate for rolling element bearings but not for the
white-metalled sleeve bearings which are used on larger elec-

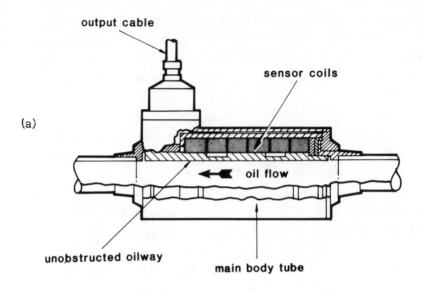

(a)

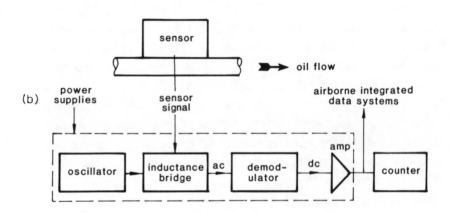

(b)

Figure 5.13 : A metal particle detector and counter
(Courtesy Smiths Industries)

a) section through the detector
b) signal processing system and counter

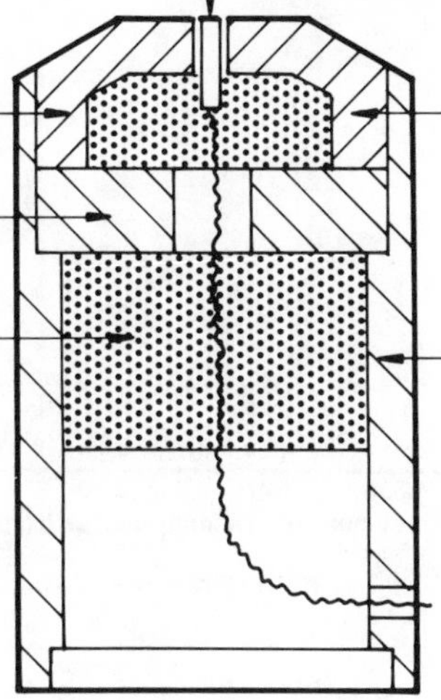

Hall effect sensor plus
┌ temperature compensating sensor

pole piece

pole piece

permanent magnet

epoxy resin

brass sleeve

Figure 5.14 : An instrumented magnetic drain plug

(Courtesy of Gabriel Microwave Systems Ltd.)

trical machines. Lloyd et al. [5.23] have investigated the problem of detecting wear in the bearings and hydrogen seals of large turbogenerator sets. They describe an investigation which characterised the debris circulating in the oil system of a number of 60 MW turbogenerators and correlated the results with plant condition. A major feature in this correlation was the presence of white-metal in the machine bearings which typically contain 85% tin. The results of their investigation showed that by determining the ratio of tin-to-iron in the debris an operator could see how much bearing damage was occurring, compared to normal running wear; see Figure 5.15. However, if information was available about running time, monitoring of tin content alone would be adequate.

Lloyd et al. then proceeded to investigate how the oil system could be automatically monitored to provide early warning of bearing damage. In particular they considered X-ray fluore-scence (XRF) detection and the measurement of the electrical

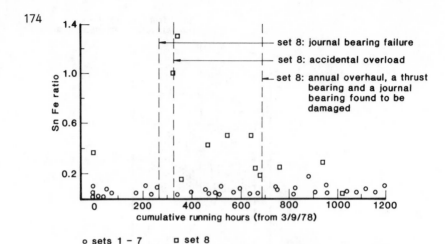

Figure 5.15 : Ratio of tin to iron in the oil filter deposits
from eight 60 MW turbogenerator sets
Taken from [5.23]

properties of the oil. Their investigation showed that XRF
would be feasible but would be prohibitively expensive as an
on-line technique. In a later paper Lloyd et al.[5.24] describe
a compromise which gives short term on-line indication of
changes in the total debris content, coupled with regular
periodic retention of debris samples for off-line examination
and analysis. They have devised an automatic sampling system,
shown in Figure 5.16, in which a filter membrane, in the form of
a tape held in a cassette, is exposed to the oil flow. Debris
is deposited on the membrane and as the pressure differential
across it reaches a preset level the tape automatically advances
to replace the clogged patch. Thus after the cassette has been
used it contains a sequence of filter patches which provide a
long term record of wear trend and debris composition. This
device is described by Cox et al.[5.25]. The off-line analysis
they describe uses XRF to determine the tin-to-iron ratio. In
many ways this is similar to the approach being adopted for core
monitors, Section 5.4.1, where the device on its own cannot be
relied upon to provide incontrovertible evidence of a fault but
must be complemented by off-line techniques.

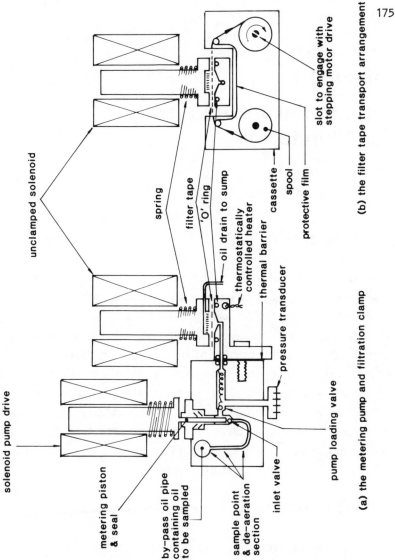

solenoid pump drive

unclamped solenoid

spring

filter tape

'O' ring

oil drain to sump

thermostatically
controlled heater

thermal barrier

cassette

spool

protective film

slot to engage with
stepping motor drive

(b) the filter tape transport arrangement

metering piston
& seal

by-pass oil pipe
containing oil
to be sampled

sample point
& de-aeration
section

inlet valve

pressure transducer

pump loading valve

(a) the metering pump and filtration clamp

Figure 5.16 : Diagram of filtration head assembly for collecting
oil debris on a filter tape cassette
Taken from [5.24]

CHAPTER 6

Vibrational Techniques
for Monitoring

6.1 INTRODUCTION

An electrical machine, its associated support structure and the
load to which it is coupled form a complex mechanical system. It
is free to vibrate at its own natural frequency, or can be forced
at many different frequencies. The result may be a level of
noise that is unacceptably high, or a progressive degree of
mechanical damage that ends in a total machine failure.
Consequently a great deal of effort has been applied to try to
determine the principal sources of vibration in electrical
machines, and a vast literature, spanning more than fifty years,
has accumulated. A representative selection of papers and
articles is included in the bibliograhy.

The principal areas of vibration in electrical machines are:

i)   the stator core response to the attractive
     force developed between rotor and stator;

ii) the response of the stator end windings to
     the electromagnetic forces on the conductors;

iii) the dynamic behaviour of the rotor;

iv) the response of the shaft bearings to vibration
transmitted from the rotor.

These four areas are obviously inter-related; for example
bearing mis-alignment or wear can quite easily result in
eccentric running which will in turn stimulate the vibrational
modes of the stator.

Before examining specific monitoring techniques we shall first
look at the characteristic features of the frequency responses of
the machine elements listed above.

6.2   STATOR CORE RESPONSE

6.2.1 General

The stator and its support structure comprise a thick-walled
cylinder, slotted at the bore, resting inside a thin-walled
structure, which may or may not be cylindrical. A stator in a
cylindrical support structure is illustrated schematically in
Figure 6.1. Analysis of a three dimensional structure such as
this, in response to the complex imposed force distribution, is a
formidable problem, even for powerful numerical techniques.
Fortunately the main features of the response can be developed
using a simplified model.

Alger [6.1] and Jordan [6.2] consider the system to be
reducible to a infinitely long, thin-walled, cylinder representing the stator core. This simplification allows a qualitative
assessment of response to be made. A fuller treatment of the
mechanical system is provided by Erdelyi [6.3], and Yang [6.4]
gives a detailed analysis of the calculation of stator displacements, taking into account the higher frequency effects due to
slot passing.

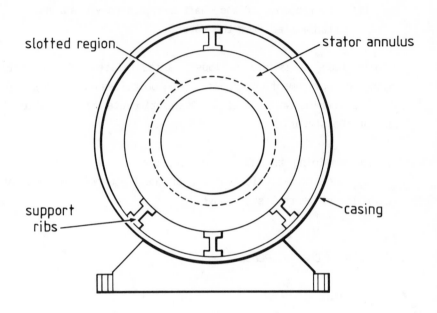

Figure 6.1 : A machine stator and its supporting structure

The forces acting on the stator core are a result of the interaction between the airgap flux wave and the currents flowing in the windings embedded in the stator slots. The forces acting on the end winding are due to the interaction between the end leakage flux and the winding currents. It is apparent, therefore, that the precise nature of the applied force waves will be a function of the form of the current distribution, and the geometry of the airgap and end region. Disturbances to either, due to rotor eccentricity or damaged areas of the rotor for example, will alter the harmonic components of the force wave and initiate a different response from the stator core, particularly if the applied forces stimulate any of the natural modes of the system.

6.2.2 Calculation Of Natural Modes

For a simple thin-walled cylinder of infinite length the displacements of the structure, at a radius fixed at the mid-wall value, may be written as,

$$u_r(\theta,t) = \sum_{n=even}^{\infty} A_n(t) \cos(n\theta) + B_n(t) \sin(n\theta) \quad \ldots (6.1)$$

and

$$u_\theta(\theta,t) = \sum_{n=even}^{\infty} C_n(t) \cos(n\theta) + D_n(t) \sin(n\theta) \quad \ldots (6.2)$$

where u_r and u_θ are the radial and peripheral displacements, respectively.

If it is further assumed that the deformations are inextensible, i.e.

$$\frac{du_\theta}{d\theta} = -u_r \qquad \ldots (6.3)$$

then

$$C_n = B_n/n \quad \text{and} \quad D_n = -A_n/n.$$

During deformation, as exhibited by the deflections given in equations (6.1) and (6.2), the system acquires elastic strain energy, and this is given by the expression,

$$V = \frac{1}{2} \int_{-\pi}^{\pi} \frac{EI}{(1-\nu^2)r^3} \left(\frac{d^2u_r}{d\theta^2} - u_r \right) d\theta \qquad \ldots (6.4)$$

where E is Young's Modulus
ν is Poisson's ratio
I is the moment of inertia of the cylinder.

Equation (6.4) reduces to,

$$V = \frac{\pi}{2} \frac{EI}{(1-\nu^2)r} \sum_{n=1}^{\infty} (1-n^2)^2 [A_n^2(t) + B_n^2(t)] \qquad \cdots (6.5)$$

Timoshenko [6.5] shows that the kinetic energy of the system will be given by,

$$T = \frac{w}{2g} \int_{-\pi}^{\pi} (\dot{u}_r + \dot{u}_\theta)d\theta \qquad \cdots (6.6)$$

where w is the weight per unit length per unit angle of the cylinder and g is the acceleration due to gravity. Substituting equations (6.1) and (6.2) into this expression gives,

$$T = \frac{\pi w}{2g} \sum_{n=1}^{\infty} \frac{n^2+1}{n^2} [\dot{A}_n^2(t) + \dot{B}_n^2(t)] \qquad \cdots (6.7)$$

If it is necessary to include the effects due to the enclosure and the frame ribs, then these can be incorporated at this stage. For example the total elastic strain energy would be given by,

$$V = V_E + V_S + V_F \qquad \cdots (6.8)$$

and the total kinetic energy by,

$$T = T_E + T_S + T_F \qquad \cdots (6.9)$$

The subscripts E, S, and F refer to the enclosure, stator core, and frame ribs respectively. The calculation of these quantities for the enclosure and frame structures may be extremely complicated, however.

The equation of motion can now be formulated. It is given for free vibration by the Euler-Lagrange equation,

$$\frac{d}{dt} \left(\frac{\partial T}{\partial \dot{A}_n} \right) - \frac{\partial V}{\partial A_n} = 0, \qquad \qquad \dots (6.10)$$

If the forced vibrational response is required directly then the right hand side of equation (6.10) must represent the forcing function. For example, if we are interested in the system response to the mth harmonic of the radial force wave $F_m(\theta,t)$, the forcing function becomes the work function,

$$W = \sum_{m=1}^{\infty} F_m(\theta,t) u_{rm}(\theta,t) d\theta \qquad \qquad \dots (6.11)$$

Generally, $F_m(\theta,t)$ has the form of a travelling wave,

$$F_m(\theta,t) = F_m \cos(\omega_m t - m\theta) \qquad \qquad \dots (6.12)$$

Reference [6.3] shows how the Rayleigh-Ritz method can be used to solve equation (6.10), to yield the natural frequencies of the system, under the assumption that time variations are harmonic. That is, the coefficients $A_n(t)$ and $B_n(t)$ are given by

$$\begin{aligned} A_n(t) &= A_n \sin\omega_0 t, \\ \text{and} \quad B_n(t) &= B_n \sin\omega_0 t. \end{aligned} \qquad \qquad \dots (6.13)$$

Under this assumption equation (6.10) becomes a polynomial in ω_0 whose roots give the natural frequencies. Some of the natural circumferential/radial mode shapes are shown in Figure 6.2.

182

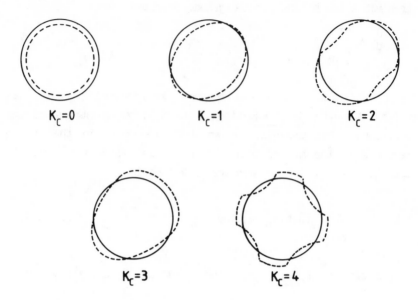

Figure 6.2 : Circumferential mode shapes of a stator

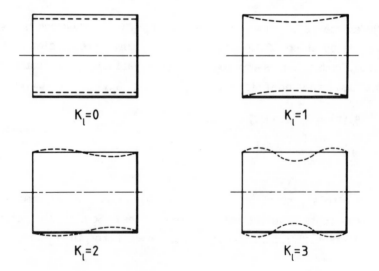

Figure 6.3 : Longitudinal mode shapes of a stator

Besides these modes it is also possible for the stator to vibrate radially as a function of machine length. The mode shapes for a cylinder vibrating in this way are illustrated in Figure 6.3. In practice, however, only the $k_\ell = 0$ case need be considered for machines of usual proportions. Very long machines may exhibit vibrations at the higher modes, but the most important mode shapes are those due to the circumferential radial vibrations. It is easily recognised that the cases for $k_c = 0$ and $k_\ell = 0$ are identical.

Approximate formulae for the natural frequencies of a simple single ring stator have been developed by Jordan et al.[6.6], and reported by Yang [6.4] in the form given here.

For $k_c = 0$, the corresponding natural frequency f_0 is given by,

$$f_0 = \frac{1}{2\pi r_m} \left[\frac{E}{\rho} \cdot \frac{w_y}{w_y + w_t + w_i + w_w} \right]^{\frac{1}{2}} \qquad \ldots (6.14)$$

with ρ the density of the core, and w_y, w_t, w_i and w_w the weights of the yoke, teeth, insulation and windings, respectively. r_m is the mean radius of the core, excluding the teeth.

For $k_c = 1$, the natural frequency f_1 is

$$f_1 = f_0 \cdot \left[\frac{2}{1 + \frac{t_0^2}{12 r_m^2} \left(\frac{w_y}{w_y + w_t + w_i + w_w} \right) M} \right]^{\frac{1}{2}} \qquad \ldots (6.15)$$

where t_0 is the thickness of the stator core annulus and M is given by the expression,

$$M = 1 + \frac{N_s}{2\pi I r_m} \left(\frac{w_t + w_w + w_i}{w_t} \right) \left(\frac{1}{3} + \frac{t_o}{2h_t} + \left(\frac{t_o}{2h_t} \right)^2 \right) a_t h_t^3 \quad \cdots \ (6.16)$$

In equation (6.16),

N_s = number of stator slots

I = the polar moment of inertia of the core

a_t = cross-section of area of the teeth

h_t = tooth depth.

The higher natural frequencies may be calculated from

$$f_m = \frac{f_o \cdot t_o m (m^2 - 1) G(m)}{2\sqrt{3} \ r_m \sqrt{m^2 + 1}} \quad \cdots \ (6.17)$$

where the function $G(m)$ is given by

$$G(m) = \left[1 + \frac{\frac{t_o^2}{12 r_m^2} (m^2 - 1) \{ m^2 (4 + \frac{w_y M}{w_y + w_t + w_i + w_w} + 3) \}}{(m^2 + 1)} \right]^{-\frac{1}{2}}$$

$$\cdots \ (6.18)$$

It is clear that the calculation of the natural frequencies of complicated mechanical structures, as represented by the stator of an electrical machine, is a difficult matter.

6.2.3 Stator Force Wave

In order to anticipate changes in stator core frame and winding vibrations due to electrical or mechanical anomalies in the machine, it is important to be able to determine the form of the exciting forces. The problem of calculating the forces exerted on the stator and rotor reduces, essentially, to one of calculating the flux density B in the airgap of the machine. This can be achieved using a numerical technique, such as the finite element method, and requires that a solution is found to the equation,

$$\nabla \times \nabla \times \underline{B} = \sigma(\underline{v} \times \underline{B} - \mu\frac{\partial B}{\partial t})$$ ... (6.19)

where σ is the electrical conductivity of the region, and $\underline{v}$ is the velocity of the rotor, relative to the travelling flux wave produced by the stator. The solution of equation (6.19), even in the two dimensions representing a cross-section in the radial and circumferential directions, requires significant computational effort if the slottings of both rotor and stator are to be taken into account. If good accuracy is a requirement it is the only suitable path to follow. Penman et al. [6.7] give a detailed explanation of the solution of equation (6.19), using the finite element technique.

The finite element method can be used to account for any distribution of windings, and any radial or peripheral geometrical variations, simply by increasing the complexity of the model. Recently Williamson and Laithwaite [6.8] proposed a circuit based method for calculating machine performance that seems to be useful for estimating the torque applied to the rotor.

Using these techniques it is possible to see the effects of windings faults and rotor eccentricity on the flux density in the airgap. Both methods are essentially numerical and therefore quantitative. Often a qualitative assessment is more valuable however, and this is readily achieved using simpler, less accurate methods, in certain circumstances.

If the rotor and stator surfaces are assumed to be smooth then it is possible to solve equation (6.19) analytically in the radial and circumferential plane, provided the motional term is neglected. This approach allows the effect of individual conductor currents to be accounted for. Hague [6.9] and Stafl

[6.10] both use separation of variable techniques to calculate aigrap flux densities for a variety of configurations.

Many authors have examined the important sources of unbalanced magnetic pull (UMP) and the effect it has on vibration. In particular Binns and Dye [6.11] identify the role of static eccentricity in the production of UMP. In addition, Swann [6.12] shows how it is possible to calculate the harmonics introduced into the flux wave due to rotor eccentricity. He does this by using a conformal transformation to re-centre the rotor. A review of a considerable amount of previous work on UMP may be found in the report by Rai [6.13].

Perhaps the simplest, generally useful method of gaining a qualitative assessment of the flux wave form is that used by Yang [6.4]. Here the flux wave is calculated by simply multiplying the magneto-motive force distribution, due to the winding currents, by the permeance of the airgap:

$$\phi = mmf \cdot \Lambda \qquad \qquad \ldots (6.20)$$

Binns [6.14] points out that this procedure has limited accuracy, but within the limitations suggested by Lim [6.15] the technique is a useful one, since it can easily accommodate geometrical effects and anomalies in winding arrangements.

The permeance variation, taking into account the relative motion of the rotor with respect to the stator, can be expressed in the form of an infinite series of harmonics. If both the rotor and stator surfaces are slotted then the permeance wave has the form,

$$\Lambda(\theta,t) = \sum_{m=1}^{\infty} \sum_{n=1}^{\infty} \Lambda_{mn}{}^{\circ} \cos[(mN_r \pm nN_s)\theta - mN_r\omega_r t] \ldots (6.21)$$

with $\Lambda_{mn}°$ the amplitude of the permeance wave, m and n integers, N_s and N_r the number of stator and rotor slots respectively, and ω_r the angular speed of the rotor.

Similarly the mmf of the stator can be expressed as an infinite series of space and time harmonics. The result, which can be found in any standard text, is,

$$F_s = \sum_k \sum_\ell F_{k\ell}^s \cos[kp(\theta - \frac{\alpha_s x}{L}) - \ell\omega t - \phi] \qquad \ldots (6.22)$$

where k is the order of the space harmonic

  ℓ is the supply time harmonic

  x is the longitudinal distance from the
     centre of the machine

  L is the active length

  α_s is the skew angle of the stator

  ϕ is the phase angle of the stator mmf F_k

  p is the number of pole pairs.

Similarly the rotor mmf, referred to the stator, can be expressed as,

$$F_s = \sum_k \sum_\ell F_{k\ell}^r \cos[kp(\theta - \omega_r t - \frac{\alpha_r x}{L}) - \ell s\omega t - \phi] \qquad \ldots (6.23)$$

The quantity s represents the slip of the rotor with respect to the stator magnetic field. The total mmf can be found by adding equations (6.22) and (6.23), and the flux wave calculated by multiplying this sum by the result of equation (6.21).

Yang shows that the effect of eccentricity can be incorporated by modifying the expression for the permeance wave, reference [6.4]. He proposes the following expressions for dynamic and static eccentricity.

Permeance variations due to static eccentricity,

$$\Lambda^s_{ecc} = \sum_{n=0}^{\infty} \Lambda_{ecc}{}^o \cos(n\theta), \qquad \qquad \ldots (6.24)$$

and permeance variations due to dynamic eccentricity,

$$\Lambda^d_{ecc} = \sum_{n=0}^{\infty} \Lambda_{ecc}{}^o \cos(n\theta - \omega_{ecc}t) \qquad \ldots (6.25)$$

where ω_{ecc} is the eccentric angular velocity.

These expressions can be combined with equation (6.21) to give the permeance wave for the complete system, and the flux wave found in the manner outlined above. Ovality of the stator bore can be accounted for in a similar manner.

The expressions and methodology outlined here provide a general and relatively simple method of calculating the harmonics of the flux wave acting on the stator so that its response can be determined.

The force can be calculated from the flux density using the method of Maxwell stresses, as described by Carpenter [6.16].

The radial force is given by,

$$\sigma_r = \frac{B^2}{2\mu_0} \qquad \qquad \ldots (6.26)$$

where B is the flux density wave, calculated from the mmf and permeance waves.

6.3 STATOR END WINDING RESPONSE

The end winding structure of an electrical machine has a relatively low stiffness or compliance but relatively high and non-linear damping coefficients due to frictional contact between adjacent conductors in the structure. The stiffness may be increased by improved methods of bracing which are used in large turbogenerators or induction machines with more onerous starting duties. The motion of the stator end winding is excited by two mechanisms:-

(i) seismic excitation of the coils as encastré beams by the ovalising displacements of the stator core and displacement of the machine by its environment;

(ii) electromagnetic forces on the coils themselves due to the currents flowing in them.

These latter forces have been considered by Brandl [6.17]. The dynamics of the end winding are very complex, partly because of its complicated geometry but also because of the distributed nature of the forces applied to it and the non-linear coefficients of its response. The resultant displacements are at twice the supply frequency, f, and it is necessary to carry out a very thorough analysis to determine the mode shapes of the structures. The dynamic behaviour has been described by Ontaguro et al. [6.18].

End winding monitoring has not so far been used for routine on-line purposes but rather as a development aid to determine end winding movements on the larger machine where problems of end winding slackening may occur. A number of utilities have installed triaxial accelerometers on the end winding structures of large turbogenerators and have monitored the amplitudes of 2f vibrations at widely-spaced intervals of time in order to check that the end winding has not slackened. The displacements of end windings on large turbogenerators at up to 150 μm are quite significant during normal running, even with modern epoxy insulation systems. So these measurements are relatively straightforward to make. However, on other machines, such as induction motors, the displacements are not so large, except on starting, and require special research techniques for their measurement as described by Campbell et al.[6.19].

6.4 ROTOR DYNAMICS

We now briefly consider the motion of the rotor in response to transverse unbalanced forces, and to torsional forces, applied either due to system disturbances on the electrical side or to rotor defects within the machine.

6.4.1 Transverse Response

Rigid rotors

In order to examine the response of a rotor to unbalanced forces a distinction can be drawn between rigid and flexible rotors. Rigid rotors may be considered as a single mass acting at the bearings, and Wort [6.20] shows that the rotor and its bearings can be modelled by the differential equation,

$$(M + m_s)x + cx + kx = mr\omega^2 \qquad \qquad \ldots (6.27)$$

where

    M = mass of the rotating disc at the bearing,

    m = equivalent unbalance mass on the shaft,

    M_s = support system mass,

    r = effective radius of the equivalent unbalanced

       mass,

    c = damping constant of the support system,

    k = stiffness of the support system.

For sinusoidal motion the peak displacement is given by the solution to (6.27), and is,

$$x = \frac{mr(\frac{\omega}{\omega_0})^2}{(M+m_s)\sqrt{\left(1-(\frac{\omega}{\omega_0})^2\right)^2 + 4D^2\,(\frac{\omega}{\omega_0})^2}} \qquad \ldots (6.28)$$

with ω_0 the natural frequency of the rotor support system, given by

$$\sqrt{\frac{k}{(M+m_s)}}\,, \qquad \text{and} \qquad D + \frac{c}{2\sqrt{k(M+m_s)}}$$

If the displacement is divided by the specific unbalance e, given by

$$e = \frac{mr}{M} \qquad \ldots (6.29)$$

then its behaviour as a function of frequency is that shown in Figure 6.4.

The degree of residual unbalance is denoted by the quantity $G = e\omega$ and the permissible limits are provided by international standard ISO 1940 (1973), as shown in Figure 6.5.

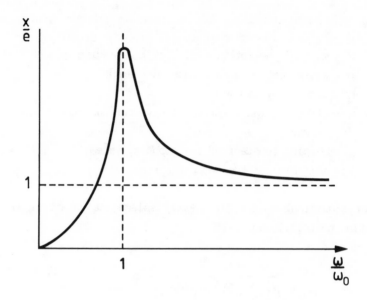

Figure 6.4 : Displacement per specific unbalance versus
normalised frequency

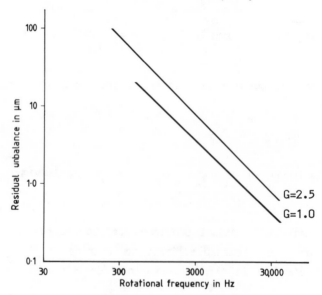

Figure 6.5 : Extract from ISO 1940 (1973) - permissible limits
to residual unbalance

For electrical machinery the appropriate quality grades are towards the lower end of the values shown in Figure 6.5. For example G = 2.5 is generally applicable to machines of all sizes, and G = 1.0 for special requirements.

Flexible rotors

For long slender rotors operating at higher speeds, as in two pole machines, particularly the larger turbogenerators which have restricted rotor radii, the foregoing analysis is insufficient, unfortunately, and the distribution of unbalance must be considered. Again reference [6.20] shows how it is possible to calculate the natural frequencies for general problems of a rotor with a flexural rigidity EI, and mass per unit length m, which are both functions of position (x). The displacement u, for any x, is given by the solution of,

$$\frac{d^2}{dx^2} \left(EI(x) \frac{d^2 u}{dx^2} \right) - \omega^2 m(x) u = \sum_{n=1}^{\infty} f_n, \qquad \ldots (6.30)$$

where f_n is the nth unbalanced force. And

$$\omega_n = \int m(x) \, g_n^2(x) \, dx, \qquad \ldots (6.31)$$

with $g_n(x)$ the nth solution of equation (6.30).

The solution for coupled systems comprising several rotors including the electrical machine and the machine it is driving or driven by is extremely complex. It is usual to assume that the stiffnesses of the couplings between rotors are low and therefore decouple each rotor, allowing them to be considered individually as described above.

The mode shapes for the rotor shafts will also depend upon the nature of the bearing supports for the shafts. For example Figure 6.6 shows the effect of hard and soft bearings on the 1st and 2nd modes for a single flexible rotor.

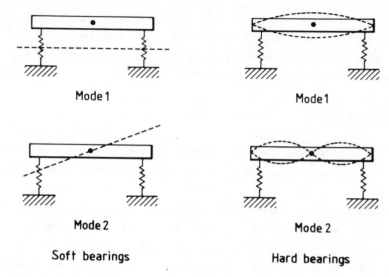

Figure 6.6 : Rotor mode shapes for hard and soft bearings

The results for higher modes are readily extrapolated from these examples. For nearly all electrical machines to which vibration monitoring would be appropriate the bearings may be considered to be hard.

The international standard limits shown in Figure 6.5 are applicable to rigid rotors operating well below their critical speed. For flexible rotors it has been suggested that the allowable eccentricity can be modified so that the same standard applies. Dimentberg [6.21] uses the correction,

$$e_{flexible} < e_{rigid}[1 - (\frac{\omega}{\omega_0})^2] \qquad \qquad \dots (6.32)$$

where ω_0 is the 1st critical speed of the rotor. This, however, is only applicable for rotors running at less than ω_0.

6.4.2 Torsional Response

The torsional oscillatory behaviour of a turbine generator, however, is extremely complicated. The generator is effectively linking a complex steam raising plant and prime mover to a large interconnected electrical network in which huge quantities of energy are being transported. The possibility for forced torsional oscillation of the rotor of the generator is clearly high because of its great length and relatively small radius, and the nature of such oscillations will depend upon the form of the disruptions that occur in either the mechanical or the electrical system. Disturbances in the electrical system are particularly important since it has been reported that they can, under some circumstances, give rise to conditions that consume shaft life due to fatigue; see Walker et al.[6.22], Joyce et al. [6.23], Hammons [6.24].

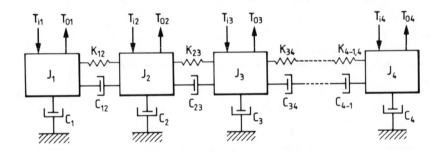

Figure 6.7 : A lumped parameter model to determine
torsional response

Cudworth et al.[6.25] have developed a computational model for a turbogenerator shaft that is very general, and allows a wide variety of fault conditions to be investigated. The electrical system is represented in phase variables and takes into account as many static and rotating electrical elements as may be required. For the mechanical system the lumped parameter model illustrated in Figure 6.7 is used. The shaft damping and steam damping effects on the turbine blades are represented by variable viscous dampers, and material damping is also included.

Representative of the results achievable using models such as the one described above is the waveform given in Figure 6.8. This shows the oscillations in shaft torque of a 500 MW generator following a phase to phase short circuit on the transmission system. The lower level oscillations obviously persist for some considerable time after the major transient has largely died away and this has obvious implications for the fatigue life of the shaft.

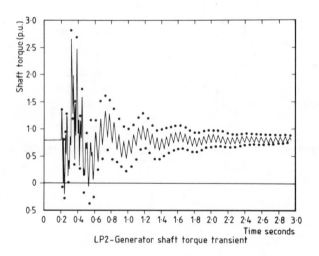

LP2-Generator shaft torque transient

Figure 6.8 : Calculated shaft torque transients using a
lumped parameter model

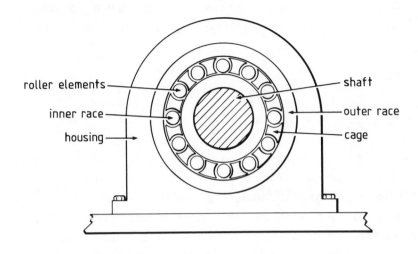

roller elements — shaft

inner race — outer race

housing — cage

Figure 6.9 : Rolling element bearing assembly

TABLE 6.1 CHARACTERISTIC FREQUENCIES OF ROLLING
ELEMENT BEARINGS

Defect	Frequency	Comment
Outer race	$\frac{n}{2} \cdot \frac{N}{60} \cdot (1 - \frac{d}{D} \cos\phi)$	Ball passing frequency on the outer race.
Inner race	$\frac{n}{2} \cdot \frac{N}{60} (1 + \frac{d}{D} \cos\phi)$	Ball passing frequency on the inner race.
Ball defective	$\frac{D}{2d} \cdot \frac{N}{60} \left[1 - (\frac{d}{D})^2 \cos^2\phi \right]$	Ball spin frequency.
Train defect	$\frac{1}{2} \cdot \frac{N}{60} (1 - \frac{d}{D} \cos\phi)$	Caused by an irregularity in the train.

n = number of balls
N = rotational speed in rev/min
d = ball diameter
D = ball pitch diameter
ϕ = ball contact angle with the races

Clearly it may be advisable to monitor such events, and methods of doing so will be discussed later in this chapter.

6.5 BEARING RESPONSE

6.5.1 General

A considerable proportion of the rotor force is transmitted to the stator via the bearings. Therefore it is important to be able to gauge the vibrational responses of the bearings to these external forces so that they may not be confused with vibrational frequencies generated by defects in the bearings themselves. External forces will result in a relative vibration of the rotor with respect to the housing and an absolute vibration of the complete bearing housing.

This action must be considered for both rolling element bearings and oil-lubricated sleeve bearings.

6.5.2 Rolling Element Bearings

A schematic view of a typical rolling element bearing is shown in Figure 6.9. The failure of bearings such as these is the commonest form of malfunction associated with smaller machines.

Because of their construction rolling element bearings produce very precisely identifiable vibrational frequencies. Also since the oil film is very thin the relative motion between the housing and the shaft is small. It is therefore possible to detect the vibrations associated with the bearings using an accelerometer mounted directly on the bearing housing.

The characteristic frequencies of such bearings depend on the geometrical size of the various elements, and can be found in many texts; see Collacott [6.26] for example. Table 6.1 summarizes these frequencies and their origins.

Besides the frequencies given in Table 6.1, there will also be higher frequencies generated by elastic deformation of the rolling elements themselves, and the excitation of the natural modes of the rings that comprise the inner and outer races. These effects will, however, be secondary to the principal components mentioned here.

The magnitudes of the components given in Table 6.1 are often lost in the general noise background when the degree of damage is small, but because of their precise nature they present an effective route for monitoring progressive bearing degradation. A simple instrument can be devised using an accelerometer mounted on the bearing housing to detect the amplitude of vibration at these characteristic frequencies. Once the characteristic frequencies have been calculated it is possible to enhance the performance of the instrument by the use of highly selective filters and weighting functions, so as to be able to identify bearing faults at an earlier stage.

When monitoring the vibration due to rolling element bearings it is always prudent to try and achieve good base-line data. This is because once the bearing becomes significantly worn the spectrum of vibration it emits becomes more random again, although at a much higher level than the base value for a good bearing. Clearly if no base line is available and no history has been built up, it is possible for specific defects to be masked by the increase in general background level.

Machinery may also exhibit a small degree of unbalance; this will tend to modulate the characteristic frequencies of the bearings and produce side bands at the rotational frequency.

Vibration monitoring is obviously highly suitable for monitoring the performance of rolling element bearings, and has gained wide acceptance throughout the industry.

6.5.3 Sleeve Bearings

In the sleeve bearing, the shaft is supported by a fluid film pumped in under high pressure between the bearing liner and the shaft by the motion of the shaft.

Now because of the compliance of the oil film and the limited flexibility of the bearing housing itself, vibrations measured at the housing may be of low amplitude. Also, because the liners of the bearing will inevitably be a soft material such as white metal, small defects are very difficult to identify by measuring the absolute vibration of the housing. These factors point to the use of displacement transducers as being the most effective tool, but they will only be useful at the lower frequencies. Higher frequencies (above 3 times the rotational frequency say) are best measured absolutely with an accelerometer mounted on the bearing housing.

It is worth bearing in mind, however, that as the bearing is more heavily loaded, due to an increase in rotor load, the thickness of the oil film will decrease with a commensurate loss in flexibility. This increases the vibration detectable at the bearing and will allow more information to be derived from the measurement.

A much more important cause for concern in the sleeve bearing is the onset of instability in the oil film. This can result in oil whirl and subsequently oil whip, in response to unusual loading of the bearing. Figure 6.10 shows the forces acting upon the shaft in a sleeve bearing, and illustrates that the shaft is supported by a wedge of oil just at the point of minimum clearance.

The oil film is circulating at a speed of approximately half the shaft speed, but because of the pressure difference on either side of the minimum clearance point, the shaft precesses at just below half speed. This motion is termed oil whirl and is a direct result of the pressure difference mentioned above, which comes about due to viscous loss in the lubricant.

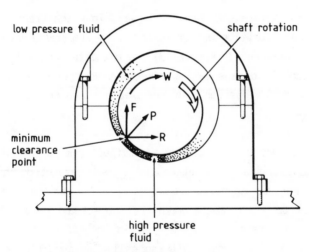

R = Reaction
F = Destabilizing components
P = Pressure
W = Whirl force

Figure 6.10 : Forces acting upon a shaft in a sleeve bearing

Instabilities occur when the whirl frequency corresponds to the natural frequency of the shaft. Under such conditions the oil film may no longer be able to support the weight of the shaft. Details of the mechanisms involved in oil whirl, and its development into the more serious instability called oil whip, which occurs when the shaft speed is twice its natural frequency, are given by Ehrich [6.27].

Care must be taken, therefore, that either the machine does not operate at a speed higher than twice the first critical speed of the rotor shaft, or if it must, then oil whirl must be suppressed.

6.6 VIBRATION MONITORING

Now that we have discussed the ways in which translational and rotational vibration can be produced in electrical machines, and we have outlined, in Chapter 3, the principal analytical tools at our disposal to measure the effect of vibration, we can proceed to show how vibration can be used to monitor the health of machines.

Because many defects can be identified by more than one method, and because the internationally agreed standards and limits relate not to specific items of plant, but to the form of analysis to which measurement is subjected, we shall use the measurement treatment as the generic identifier. We shall also be principally concerned with so called on-condition monitoring. That is, we are interested in techniques that can be applied to machinery that is running and in the predictive power of the monitoring rather than simply the ability to merely intercept faulty conditions when they become serious enough to do damage. Naturally enough there may often be much that is common to both objectives.

6.6.1 <u>Overall Level Monitoring</u>

This simple form of monitoring is still the most commonly used technique generally speaking, although as an aid to the diagnosis of faults in electrical machines it is a fairly limited one. The measurement taken is simply the rms value of the vibration level over a preselected bandwidth. The usual bandwidth is 10 Hz to 1 kHz, or 10 Hz to 10 kHz, and in practice the measurement parameter is vibration velocity taken at the bearing cap of the machine under surveillance. The technique has found favour because over the years a considerable statistical base regarding machinery failures has been built up. This has resulted in the publication of recommended running vibration standards. These standards do not attempt to give diagnostic information, but simply an indication of overall health. Many operators use a strategy, based on such information, to aid maintenance scheduling.

The guidance given by Vibration Standard VDI 2056 which is given in Brüel & Kjær [6.28], is illustrated below in Table 6.2. These criteria are based solely on machine rating and support systems, and utilize a 10 Hz to 1 kHz bandwidth. Essentially it recommends that when vibration levels change by 8 dB or more care must be exercised, and when the change exceeds 20 dB action should follow. These limits can be relaxed however if a subsequent frequency analysis shows that the cause of the increase in level is due to a rise in the higher frequency components. In such cases changes of 16 dB and 40 dB respectively may be more appropriate figures.

Another useful set of criteria is that given in the Canadian Government specification CDA/MS/NVSH107 also given in [6.28]. This specification relates primarily to measurements taken on bearings, and it is here that overall level measurement is most commonly employed. This specification has a broader bandwidth

TABLE 6.2 : VIBRATIONAL STANDARD VDI 2056

Vibration Severity Criteria (10 Hz-1kHz)
VDI 2056, ISO 2372, BS 4675

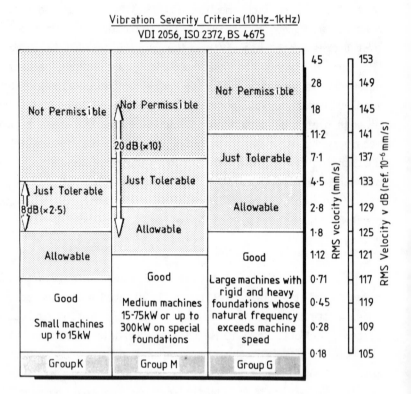

(Courtesy of Brüel and Kjær)

than VDI 2056, namely 10 Hz to 10 kHz, but still relies on overall velocity vibration measurement. A section of the specification, as it relates to electrical machines, is given below in Table 6.3.

The strength of the overall level technique is its simplicity. It requires only the simplest of instrumentation, and because of this it is a common feature in many installations. It also provides an ideal method for use with portable instruments, but it makes heavy demands upon technical personnel. The sensitivity of the technique is also low, particularly when a defect is at an early stage, and there is little help on offer to aid diagnosis without further sophisticated techniques being employed.

However, the Neale Report [6.29] indicates that it may be possible to effect a limited diagnosis by taking two overall level measurements: V_a, the peak velocity, and X the peak to peak displacement. These quantities are then used to define the parameter

$$F = \frac{0.52 \ NX}{V_a} \qquad \qquad \ldots (6.33)$$

where N is the speed, in rev/min, of the machine.

Accordingly, the interpretations suggested by Table 6.4 may be appropriate.

6.6.2 Frequency Spectrum Monitoring

Undoubtedly the key to diagnostics, using vibration monitoring, is the frequency spectrum of the received signal, and the past decade has seen a remarkable increase in the range and sophistication of techniques and instrumentation available for spectral analysis.

TABLE 6.3   VIBRATION LIMITS FOR MAINTENANCE AS GIVEN IN CANADIAN
GOVERNMENT STANDARD CDA/MS/NVSH107 [6.31]

Type of plant	New Machines		Worn Machines (full load operation)	
	100-1000 hr life	1000-10000 hr life	Service Level	Overhaul* immediately
	All measurements in mm sec^{-1}			
Boiler auxiliaries	1.0	3.2	5.6	10.0
Large steam turbines	1.8	18.0	18.0	32.0
Motor-generator sets	1.0	3.2	5.6	10.0
Pump drives	1.4	5.6	10.0	18.0
Fan drives at far end	1.0	3.2	5.6	10.0
Motors (general)	0.25	1.8	3.2	5.6

*   In this column the levels must not be exceeded in any octave
band.

TABLE 6.4   DIAGNOSIS USING OVERALL LEVEL MEASUREMENTS
BASED ON THE NEALE REPORT [6.31]

Value of F	Trend	Defect
F < 1	Decreasing	Oil whirl.
F = 1	Steady	Unbalance - indicative of eccentricity or perhaps faulty rotor cage.
F > 1	Increasing	Misalignment - static eccentricity.

There are various levels of spectral analysis commonly used, and these may be regarded as a continuum extending from the overall level reading to the narrow band with constant frequency bandwidth presentation, as shown in Figure 6.11.

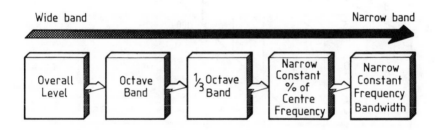

Figure 6.11 : Levels of spectral analysis

In the octave band and 1/3 octave band techniques the spectrum is split into discrete bands, as defined by Table 6.5. The bands are, by definition, such that when the frequency is scaled logarithmically the bands are of equal width. The constant percentage band is one which is always the same percentage of the centre frequency, whilst the constant frequency bandwidth is an absolutely fixed bandwidth form of analysis which can give very high resolution, provided the instrumentation is of a sufficiently high specification.

TABLE 6.5 : OCTAVE AND THIRD OCTAVE BANDS

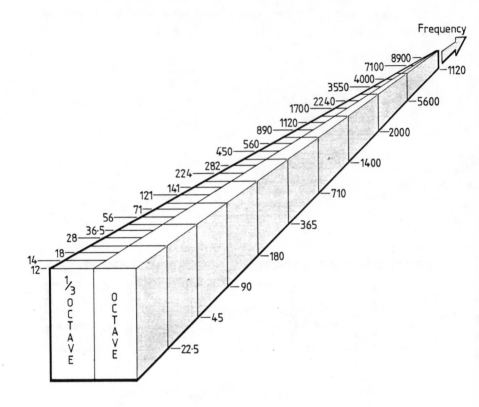

The effect that the change of bandwidth has on the processed signal output highlights precisely why the narrow band techniques are superior to the overall level technique as diagnostic tools. For example, a certain transducer may provide an output that may be interpreted in the ways shown in Figure 6.12. It is apparent that the components around frequency f_1 dominate the overall level reading, and the shape of the 1/3 octave result. Important changes, say of f_2 and f_3, or even the presence of other components,could go largely unnoticed except by the use of narrow band methods. This is crucial because the flexibility of the system may be such that important components are masked by those closer to resonances in the mechanical structure of the machine.

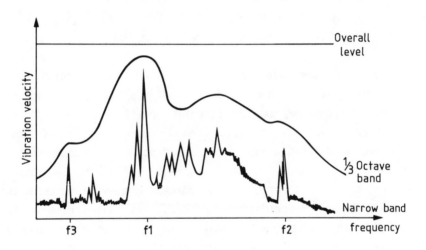

Figure 6.12 : Effect of change in bandwidth on spectral response

The narrow band spectrum also allows the operator to trend the condition of the machine most effectively. This requires that an initial base-line spectrum is taken and subsequent spectra are compared with it. The use of digitally derived spectra means that the results of such comparisons can be computed quickly since the spectra reduce to a simple sequence of numbers at discrete frequencies, as closely spaced as required within the limitations of the instrumentation.

In this way criteria such as VDI 2056 can be applied for each frequency.

Because of the large amounts of data generated using narrow band methods, it is frequently convenient to predetermine the operational limits, on the basis of one of the vibration standards, and to construct an operational envelope around the base line spectrum. This can take account of the wider limits allowable at higher frequencies, and can be used to automatically flag warnings when maintenance limits are reached.

The basis of this technique is illustrated in Figure 6.13.

The techniques described thus far, in this Section, are relatively general. In order to identify not just unsatisfactory overall performance, but to pinpoint specific problems, it is necessary to examine discrete frequencies, or groups of frequencies, as indicated earlier in this chapter. Induction motors in particular require a high degree of frequency resolution applied to their vibration signals since the speed of rotation is close to the electrical supply frequency. This tends to generate sidebands spaced at s and 2s around the harmonics of the supply frequency, where s is the slip frequency of the machine. The application of vibration monitoring for fault diagnosis in large turbogenerators has been described by Mayes et al. [6.30] and computer analysis techniques which can be applied off-line to vibration data collected on-line are described by Herbert [6.31].

6.6.3 Defects Detectable From The Stator Force Wave

Using the techniques in the previous Section and verifying by measurement, it has been shown that UMP can excite components at 1, 2, and 4 times the fundamental frequency. Dynamic unbalance and coupling misalignment also produce this effect; see Rai [6.13], Erskine [6.32] and Leonard et al. [6.33]. The last

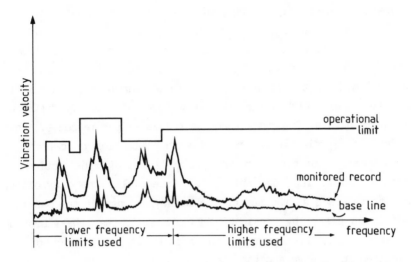

Figure 6.13 : Operational envelope around a spectral response

reference also suggests that the even orders of the fundamental occur in the frame vibration spectrum due to inter-turn winding faults on the stator. Cameron et al.[6.34] use the principal slot harmonics as an indicator of eccentric running. They suggest that the frequencies to seek are given by,

$$f_m = [(nN_r \pm k_e) \frac{1-s}{p} \pm q] \qquad \ldots (6.34)$$

where n is any integer, q is zero or even, and k_e is the so called eccentricity order number, which is zero for static eccentricity and a low integer value for dynamic eccentricity. They report tests on a machine with a 51 slot rotor (N_r), and a 4-pole, 3-phase stator, which exhibits an increase in frame vibration levels of 25 dB and 17 dB at the frequencies 1104 Hz and 1152 Hz due to the introduction of 50% dynamic eccentricity.

There are obviously strong indications that frame vibration can be used to monitor a variety of fault conditions, particularly in induction machines. Caution must be exercised, however, for transmitted vibration from adjacent, or coupled, plant may excite a natural mode in the machine, while a force component which results due to a fault within the machine may be sufficiently different from any natural frequency to cause only a slight response. This effective signal-to-noise ratio for the detection of defects by frame-borne vibration can be quantified using the notion of system flexibility (or mobility). Essentially the flexibility may be regarded as the sum of the modal response of the machine, and it is clear, by considering Figure 6.14, that the vibration experienced by an element in the machine is the product of the exciting force wave and the flexibility.

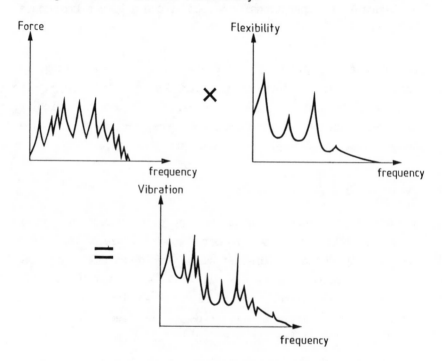

Figure 6.14 : The effect of structural flexibility on vibration

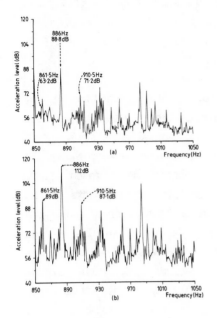

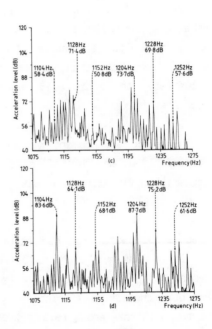

Figure 6.15 : Spectra of stator frame vibration

a) 28 rotor slots, 4 pole machine - uniform airgap
b) 28 rotor slots, 4 pole machine - 80% static eccentricity
c) 51 rotor slots, 4 pole machine - uniform airgap
d) 51 rotor slots, 4 pole machine - 50% dynamic eccentricity

(with permission of IEE)

A number of authors have reported the identification of various vibrational frequencies associated with defects in induction machines, including Rai [6.13], Erskine [6.32], Leonard et al.[6.33 and 6.34], Maxwell [6.35] and Hargis et al.[6.36].

It has been suggested by Rai [6.13] that vibration at (or near) 50 Hz, 100 Hz and 200 Hz is indicative of eccentricity, but the picture is confused because other anomalies also manifest themselves by the production of such frequencies, for example misalignment and dynamic unbalance. Leonard and Thompson [6.33, 6.34] also show that 100 Hz, 200 Hz and 300 Hz components can be expected when the stator frame vibration is monitored during the occurrence of an inter-turn winding fault or supply voltage unbalance (including single phasing). They also show that higher order harmonics, as derived from equation 6.34, occur in the stator frame vibration, due to eccentricity. This is clearly illustrated in Figure 6.15, which shows results taken on test machines.

The exact arrangement of the drive, and the nature of the coupled load, may be of critical importance, however, since transmitted vibration may mask the frequency which one is hoping to measure.

Obviously, vibration can occur in electrical machinery as a result of either electrical or mechanical action. In order to summarise the dominant frequencies for a given defect, Table 6.6 has been compiled, principally by distilling the information to be found in references [6.37, 6.29, and 6.38].

6.6.4 Torsional Oscillation Monitoring

As we have outlined previously in Section 6.4.2, there may be a specific need to monitor the torsional behaviour of long thin machine shafts such as on a turbine generator. The direct

TABLE 6.6 VIBRATIONAL FREQUENCIES RELATED TO SPECIFIC
ELECTRICAL MACHINE FAULTS

Fault type	Important Frequencies	Comments
Unbalanced rotor	f_r	Very common – also causes unbalanced magnetic pull which gives $2f_r$ vibration.
Misalignment of rotor shaft	f_r, $2f_r$, $3f_r$, $4f_r$	Also manifests as static eccentricity; therefore see components generated from this source, below.
General looseness of shaft in bearing housing	f_r, f_r, $2f_r$	Generates a clipped time waveform; therefore produces a high number of harmonics.
Oil whirl and whip in sleeve bearings	$(0.43 \text{ to } 0.48)f_r$	Pressure fed bearings only.
Rolling element bearing damage	See equations in Table 6.1 for exact frequencies. Also frequencies in the range 2-60 kHz due to element resonance.	Common source of vibration. Bearing faults can also be diagnosed using the Shock Pulse Method.

TABLE 6.6 (contd.)

Fault type	Important Frequencies	Comments
General electrical problems	nf_r, nf_s	A problem can usually be identified as having electrical origins by simply removing the supply. If the fault disappears then the problem is associated with the electrical aspect of the machine.
Eccentricity in induction machines	As defined by equation 6.34 + those components due to unbalanced rotor.	Sidebands at ±1 x slip frequency may also occur.
Broken rotor bars in induction machines	$f_r \pm 2sf_s$	May be difficult to detect due to the low level. Speed, leakage field or current changes may be preferred as a monitoring parameter.
Stator winding faults	f_s $2f_s$, $4f_s$	Difficult to differentiate between fault types using vibration monitoring alone.
D.C. machine commutator faults	kf_r	Unbalanced rotor components can also be generated.

f_r = rotational frequency
f_s = supply frequency
n = an integer
k = number of commutation sequence
s = slip

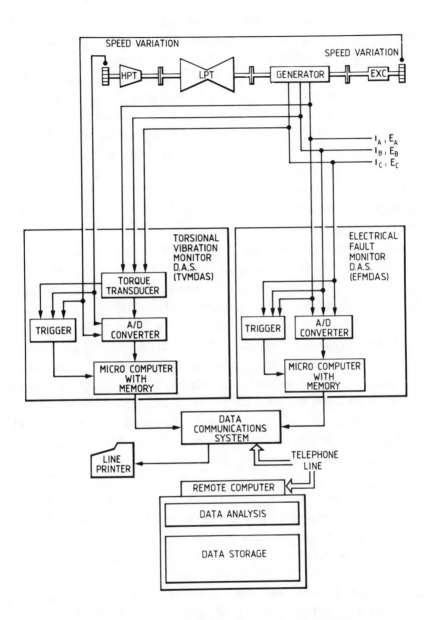

Figure 6.16 : A shaft torsional oscillation monitoring system

approach to this problem would be to mount suitable strain gauges on the shaft, together with suitable telemetry, to transmit the gauge output from the rotating reference frame. This has only been done for experimental purposes and is not appropriate for long term use due to the harsh operational conditions the transducers would need to withstand. Two indirect methods of monitoring the torsional responses of shafts have been outlined by Rusche [6.39] and Home et al. [6.40]. The monitoring system proposed in reference [6.40] is illustrated in Figure 6.16, in which it can be seen that the twist of the shaft system is measured by comparing the angular displacement of the non-drive end of the high pressure turbine shaft with that of the non-drive end of the generator exciter. The airgap torque produced by the machine is calculated directly from the monitored electrical quantities. The monitor has a modular construction, the two principal elements being concerned with the capture of the mechanical (or torque) transient and the electrical transient. The torque transient capture unit is triggered by any sudden increase in the airgap torque, or by sudden changes in the shaft angular vibrational velocities. Similarly the electrical transient is captured in response to any sudden change in the value of the line currents. The captured data can then be transmitted over standard telephone links to a central computing installation for further analysis and evaluation.

The software residing in the central computing installation receives the captured data and determines the torsional response of the shaft and the associated impact on the fatigue life of the set. The results obtained in this way can be used to plan maintenance intervals on the basis of need, rather than risk catastrophic failure when there has been a high level of system disturbances between fixed outages. The function of the monitoring system is outlined in Figure 6.17.

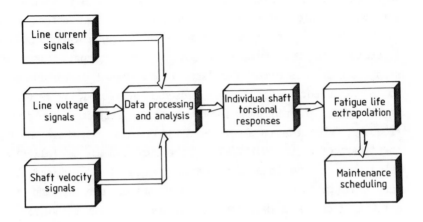

Figure 6.17 : Functional description of torsional
oscillation monitoring system

The monitoring of torsional oscillations can also be used to detect defects in induction motors. The speed of an induction motor driving an ideal load should be constant. Perturbations in load and defects within the rotor circuit of the machine will cause the speed to fluctuate. If the rotor is defective the speed fluctuation will occur at twice slip frequency. This is because the normally torque-producing slip frequency currents that flow in the rotor winding are unable to flow through the defective part. In effect the speed fluctuations complement the twice slip frequency current fluctuation described in Chapter 4. A defective induction machine with a rotor of infinite inertia will have twice slip frequency current fluctuations and no speed variation, whereas a low inertia rotor will exhibit speed fluctuations but no current fluctuation. Gaydon et al. [6.36, 6.41, 6.42] have measured these fluctuations directly with an instrument that uses a signal averaging technique locked to the slip frequency of the motor. A once-per-revolution pulse is

required from the motor shaft, using either an optical or
magnetic sensor. This enables the rotational period of the shaft
to be measured to a precision of 1 µs. Figure 6.18 shows how the
rotational period will be perturbed by a typical defect in a
rotor. The small changes in shaft period are converted by the
instrument to the normalised quantity 'fractional change in
slip', and this is directly related to the amount of rotor damage
to be expected. For effective signal averaging, a reference
signal at slip frequency is obtained by strobing the supply
frequency with the once-per-revolution pulse, as shown in the
lower part of Figure 6.18. This is a rare example of 'aliasing'
being used to advantage. The technique has similar capabilities
for detecting rotor defects to the stator current and flux
analysis techniques described in Chapter 4. The technique has
generally been used to survey motors and provide a statement on
the number of broken rotor bars present. However, a recent

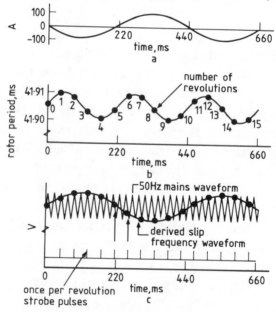

Figure 6.18 : Motor speed fluctuation waveforms
a) Current in healthy bar - normally ummeasurable
b) Shaft period - slows down and speeds up at twice slip
    frequency
c) 50 Hz supply strobed once per rev. to give slip
    reference

development has been to produce an instrument that can communicate over an IEEE-488 bus; the instrument rapidly measures the motor speed fluctuation and passes the data to a proprietary portable computer. For permanent installation a scanner can be added to the bus so that every large motor on a site can be checked for rotor defects automatically several times each day. The prototype of this instrument called Rotach is presently undergoing service trials.

6.6.5 Shock Pulse Monitoring

The shock pulse method is used exclusively for detecting defects in rolling element bearings and is based upon the principles described in Section 6.5.2. Since a large number of electrical machine failures occur due to bearing problems, we shall indicate the main features of the technique.

As a rolling element bearing deteriorates, the moving surfaces develop small pits. The interaction between such surfaces generates stress waves, known as shock pulses. These shock pulses are at ultrasonic frequencies and can be detected by piezoelectric transducers with a strongly resonant frequency characteristic. The usual frequency of operation is around 32 kHz. To further increase sensitivity the electronic conditioning for the transducer is tuned to the same resonant frequency. A peak holding circuit enables the maximum value of shock to be recorded. It is claimed that this reading is a good measure of the condition of the bearing.

This condition of the bearing is assessed by defining a quantity known as the shock pulse value, SPV, defined as:-

$$SPV = \frac{R}{n^2 F^2} \qquad \qquad \dots (6.35)$$

where R is the meter reading, n is the shaft speed, and F is a factor relating to bearing geometry. Low values indicate bearings in good condition

Generally the technique is best used in conjunction with overall level monitoring, and Table 6.7 can be used to give qualitative guidance on the bearing condition.

TABLE 6.7   SHOCK PULSE INTERPRETATION

Overall Vibration Level Trend	Shock Pulse Value Trend	Comments
Low and rising	Remains low	No bearing damage.
Low and rising	Low but rising at same rate as overall level	Bearing damage likely.
Low and rising	High value but remaining constant	Damaged bearing but other problem causing rise in level.

Schoel [6.43] also suggests that it is possible to determine the relative thickness of the lubricant film in roller element bearings, using the shock pulse method, and indeed he proposes a monitoring system to do this. The technique is based on the experimental evidence that the shock pulse value increases in approximately the manner shown in Figure 6.19, as a function of the percentage of dry contact time per revolution. The dry contact time was measured by monitoring current flow between the inner and outer races of a test bearing and current flow taken as an indication of dry contact.

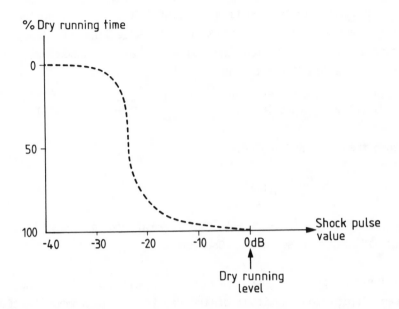

Figure 6.19 : Shock pulse value as a function of dry running
time per revolution

Quantitative evaluation using the shock pulse method remains
difficult, however.

6.6.6 Special Vibration Monitoring Techniques

In addition to the more conventional vibration monitoring
techniques described elsewhere in Section 6.6 there are a number
of specialised techniques and two shall be briefly mentioned
here. Although they are beginning to establish themselves as
powerful diagnostic tools, their acceptance and, subsequently,
their application, is limited primarily at the moment to the
diagnosis of faults in gearboxes.

Cepstrum analysis

Mathematically the cepstrum, $C(\tau)$ of a function is described as the inverse Fourier transform of the logarithm of the power spectrum of the function; i.e. if we define the power spectrum $P(f)$ of a function $g(t)$ as

$$P_{gg}(f) = F\{g(t)\}^{2} \qquad\qquad \ldots (6.36)$$

then the corresponding cepstrum is

$$C(\tau) = F^{-1}\{\log P_{gg}(f)\} \qquad\qquad \ldots (6.37)$$

where F and F^{-1} represent the forward and backward Fourier transforms, as described in Chapter 3.

The dimension of the parameter τ is obviously time; hence we can display the magnitude of the cepstrum with respect to time intervals in the same way as the spectrum can be illustrated with respect to frequency.

The use of the cepstrum has found favour in examining the behaviour of gear boxes because such items of equipment tend to produce many families of side bands in their vibration spectra, due to the variety of meshing frequencies and shaft speeds that may be present. The cepstrum essentially highlights periodicity in complicated signals, and hence identifies clearly various families of sidebands. The identification of various sidebands in a rich signal may be practically impossible using spectral analysis, but as Figure 6.20 shows the cepstrum easily picks them out. This Figure is reproduced from Randall [6.44], which also provides an excellent review of the use of cepstrum analysis applied to gearboxes.

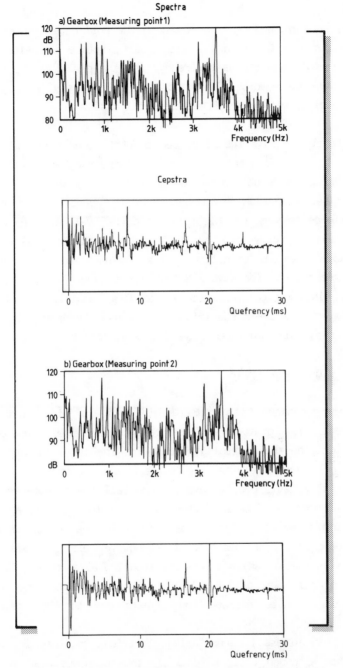

Figure 6.20 : Vibration spectra and associated cepstra for
two measurement points on a gear box
(Courtesy of Brüel and Kjær)

We note in passing that although the horizontal scales of the cepstrum are in seconds it is usual practice to refer to the horizontal quantity as quefrency, and the peaks in the cepstrum as the rahmonics. This is done to firmly identify the methodology with that of spectral analysis.

Clearly if this technique can identify side bands with ease, then it may hold significant possibilities for the identification of faults in induction machines, particularly when they are fed from harmonic rich inverters. To the best of the authors' knowledge no work on this application has yet been reported but it may yet prove to be a fruitful path to follow. Its disadvantages lie principally with the undeniable complexity of the technique. It is very definitely a 'post' spectral analysis tool, in much the same way as spectral analysis is generally employed once one's suspicions are aroused by anomalies in time domain signals taken using overall level monitoring.

Time signal averaging

This technique is a valuable aid to identifying which moving element in a gearbox a fault relates to. It does this by synchonizing the averaging process for the incoming signal to a time reference relating to a particular element. As seen previously, this process averages out all the components due to the elements moving at different speeds to the reference. By locking on to each element speed in turn, the condition of each can be checked. A word of caution, however, because some thought shows us that if any elements are rotating at a speed which is an integer multiple, or sub-multiple, of the reference then we will not be able to exclude the effects due to these elements.

Its usefulness for monitoring electrical machines is somewhat limited although it is effectively the technique used by Gaydon et al. [6.36] in the instrument which detects rotor cage broken bars by measuring the variation in rotational period of the machine. It may also prove helpful for drive systems where the effect of the gearbox, excluding of course the input shaft and bearings, can be removed using this technique.

The method, by its nature, could not easily be used for trend monitoring. It would theoretically be possible to store spectrally transformed versions of the averaged time signals, at discrete time intervals, and deduce information from these. There are no documented reports of this having been tried, however. Essentially, the technique is a diagnostic one only.

CHAPTER 7
Temperature Monitoring

7.1 INTRODUCTION

As has been described in Chapter 2 the limits to rating of electrical machines are generally set by the maximum permissible temperature which the insulation can withstand. Indeed the performance testing of machines, before they leave a manufacturer's works, is dominated by the measurement of winding or embedded temperatures and the need to achieve temperature rises within the appropriate standards. The measurement of temperature therefore has an important place in the monitoring of electrical machines.

There are three basic approaches to temperature monitoring:-

(i)   to measure local temperatures at points in the machine using embedded temperature detectors;

(ii) to use a thermal image, fed with suitable variables, to monitor the temperature of what is perceived to be the hottest spot in the machine;

(iii)   to measure   distributed temperatures in the
        machine or the bulk temperatures of coolant
        fluids.

These approaches demonstrate the fundamental difficulty of
thermal monitoring, which is resolving the conflict between the
fact that point temperature measurements are easy to make, but
give only local information, whereas bulk temperature measurements are more difficult and run the risk that local hot-spots
can be overlooked.

The following three Sections show how these approaches can be
applied practically.

7.2 LOCAL TEMPERATURE MEASUREMENT

This can be done using thermocouples or resistance temperature
detectors (RTD) whose characteristics are described in Chapter 3.
To monitor the active part of the machine they are usually
embedded in the stator winding, and in the stator core. They can
also be located in the bearings, to detect hot running.   The
choice of location requires careful consideration during the
specification stage of the machine.   For example temperature
detectors embedded in the stator winding need to be located close
to its hottest part, which may be in the slot portion or end
winding portion depending on the thermal design of the machine.
Or for a machine with an asymmetrical cooling arrangement they
should be located at the hottest end of the machine.   Say [7.1]
gives some guidance to where embedded temperature detectors
(ETDs) should be located and this is summarised in Figure 7.1.
It should be noted that where ETDs are fitted in bearings,
precautions must be taken to ensure that the bearing insulation
is not breached.

230

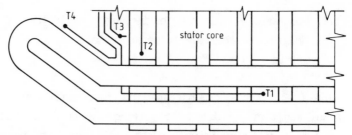

a) embedded between conductors in the slot portion (T1)
   embedded in core pack laminations (T2)
   mounted on potentially hot components such as pressure plates (T3)
   embedded on conductors in the end winding portion (T4)

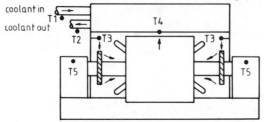

b) water or air inlet to the heat exchanger (T1)
   water or air outlet from the heat exchanger (T2)
   re-entry air to the machine from the heat exchanger (T3)
   exhaust air from the machine to the heat exchanger (T4)
   bearing temperatures (T5)

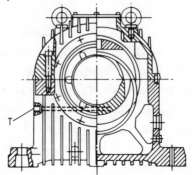

c) bearing temperature (T)

Figure 7.1 : Location of temperature detectors in
electrical machines

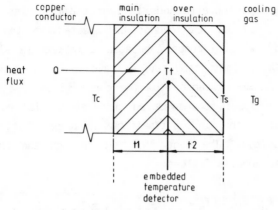

a) asymmetrically embedded temperature detector

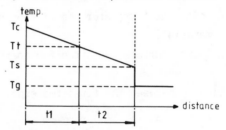

b) temperature detection from a)

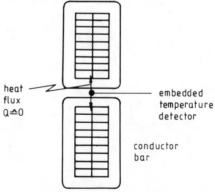

c) symmetrically embedded temperature detector

Figure 7.2 : Effect of embedding a temperature detector
away from an active part

The weakness of these methods is that thermocouples and RTDs are metallic devices and cannot be located on the hottest component, the winding copper, because they require electrical isolation. On a winding the devices have to be embedded in the insulation at some distance from the copper itself, see Figure 7.2(a). As a result the measured temperature will not necessarily be that of the winding itself but an image of it, as shown in Figure 7.2(b). The heat flow, Q, through the insulation system is described as follows:-

$$Q = h(T_s - T_g) = \frac{k}{t_2} (T_s - T_t) = \frac{k}{t_1} (T_a - T_c) \qquad (7.1)$$

where k is the heat transfer coefficient of the insulating
material,
h is the surface heat transfer coefficient.

Eliminating T_s between the first two expressions gives:-

$$T_t = Q(\frac{t_2}{h} + \frac{1}{k}) - T_g \qquad (7.2)$$

therefore

$$T_t = h \ (\frac{T_c - T_t}{t_1})(\frac{t_2}{h} + \frac{1}{k}) \ - T_g \qquad (7.3)$$

$$T_t = \frac{T_c(\frac{t_2}{t_1} + \frac{h}{kt_1}) - T_g}{1 + (\frac{t_2}{t_1} + \frac{h}{kt_1})} \qquad (7.4)$$

So

$$T_t \simeq T_c , \qquad \text{if } (\frac{t_2}{t_1} + \frac{h}{kt_1}) \ \gg 1$$

i.e. if $t_2 + \frac{h}{k} \gg t_1$ $\hspace{4cm}$ (7.5)

So the measured temperature T_t will approach the temperature of the active part T_c if the thickness of insulation, t_2, applied over the ETD is sufficiently great compared to the main insulation. This problem does not occur for devices embedded in the slot portion, between two conductors, as shown in Figure 7.2(c) where there is a negligible heat flux between the active copper parts. But it is an important difficulty when monitoring end winding temperatures in which case the thickness of overtaped insulation, t_2, needs to be substantial if a sensible reading is to be obtained.

It would be very desirable to develop a temperature monitoring device which can be affixed to a high voltage winding and give electrical isolation. Such a device has been developed for power transformers by Hampton et al. [7.2] and is known as the Vapotherm. It comprises a small phial of liquid which has a high vapour pressure that varies widely with temperature. The phial is affixed to the high voltage winding whose temperature is required. The pressure in the phial is then monitored through a non-conducting silicone rubber tube and the temperature is derived electronically from the pressure measurement. The device has been applied, on a trial basis, to operational transformers where it has performed satisfactorily. It is not certain that its performance would be as good mounted on the end winding of a rotating machine where the vibration amplitude is considerable and high air flows exist that could damage the connecting tube.

Alternative methods of measuring temperature on high voltage components are also being developed where isolation is achieved using fibre-optic techniques. A particular design using the dependence of the polarisation of light on the temperature of a material is described by Rogers [7.3] and shown in Figure 7.3.

234

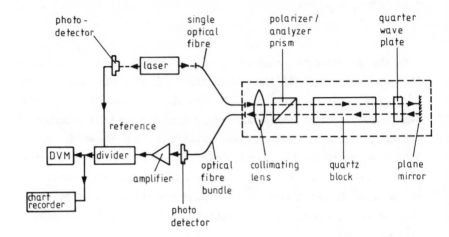

Figure 7.3 : Fibre optic temperature detector
Taken from [7.3]

Light from a laser is transmitted to the device and is passed
through a polarising prism before being launched into a block of
material maintained at the temperature to be measured. This
material introduces a rotation of the light beam which is
dependent on temperature. The beam is reflected back through the
block and polarizer and is relaunched into the fibre with a light
amplitude proportional to the polarization which has taken place
in the block. By arranging two passes through the block the
polarisation is rendered insensitive to electrical or magnetic
field effects.

The temperature measurements described so far have all been on
stationary parts of the machine and on many machines the design
is thermally stator-critical, so the hottest spot will be located
there. But many machines are rotor-critical, particularly larger
induction motors, because under stall conditions the rotor losses
are very large, and the temperatures can rise rapidly to values
which could damage the rotor insulation and jointing. On such

machines there may well be no apparent deterioration after one or two stalls, but should this occur repeatedly there will be a weakening of rotor bars and/or end rings which may result in premature mechanical failure. In the past there have been various crude methods of measuring rotor temperatures for experimental purposes using heat-sensitive papers or paints, or thermocouples connected through slip rings. Until recently, however, there has not been a method sufficiently reliable to use for monitoring purposes. Geszti [7.4] has described a technique using optical coupling between the rotor and a decoding unit on the stator. Siyambalapitiya et al.[7.5] have described a similar device for monitoring eight thermocouples, multiplexing the signal on the rotor, then optically coupling to the stator and decoding in a microcomputer. A schematic diagram of the instrument is shown in Figure 7.4. The intention is that the device should become part of a monitoring scheme for a rotor-critical machine.

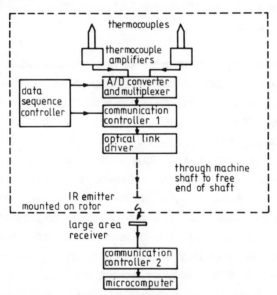

Figure 7.4 : Schematic diagram of a rotor temperature monitoring device
Taken from [7.5]

7.3 HOT-SPOT MEASUREMENT AND THERMAL IMAGES

Local temperature measurements give the machine operator
considerable confidence that he knows the operating temperature
of key points in the machine, but there is always the nagging
suspicion that temperature detectors may not be located at the
hottest point. This problem has long been recognised in power
transformers where it is extremely difficult to obtain even
embedded winding temperatures because of the great thickness of
electrical isulation necessary on EHV windings, and so thermal
images of the hot spot temperature are used. The thermal image
consists of a dial-type thermometer with its bulb immersed in the
region where the transformer oil is hottest. A small heating
coil, connected to the secondary of a current-transformer, serves
to circulate round the bulb a current proportional to the load
current and is such that it increases the bulb temperature by an
amount equal to the greatest winding-to-coil temperature gra-
dient. The indicator therefore registers an approximation to the
hot-spot temperature.

The thermal image technique has not received wide application
on rotating electrical machines, although it deserves to. The
availability of a thermal image hot-spot temperature of a machine
could be used for motor protection purposes and a guide to these
problems is given by Ramsden and Dring [7.6]. Mellor et al.[7.7]
have proposed such a technique for small, totally enclosed,
forced-cooled, induction motors where a thermal model of the
machine is configured in a microprocessor which is fed with
signals proportional to the ambient air temperature and the
stator winding current. The model can calculate the predicted
temperatures at a variety of key points in the machine. Stator
core, stator winding slot, or stator endwinding representation
must be programmed solely using the design information for the
machine. The instrument is designed to produce an analogue that
is proportional to several temperatures at the hottest points.

Mellor et al. have used the device on two TEFC machines and compared the predictions of the thermal image with the actual measured temperatures in the stator endwinding which was found to be the hottest point in this design of the machine. Figure 7.5 shows the comparison of results for those two machines when they have been put through very severe duty cycles and it can be seen that the results are extremely good. The device has been designed to be part of the thermal protection of a motor but it could equally well be used for monitoring a machine for operational purposes, particularly, for example, on a crucial machine located in an inaccessible position, where hot-spot measurements may be difficult to obtain.

7.4 BULK MEASUREMENT

In the electrically active part of the machine, even when hot-spot locations are known or hot-spot temperatures can be surmised from a thermal image, there is still a desire to obtain a bulk indication of the thermal state of the machines. This can be found from the measurement of the internal and external coolant temperature rises, obtained from thermocouples located, for example, as shown in Figure 7.1. This is done on most larger machines but it is normal for coolant temperatures to be displayed and rare for the point values to be subtracted to give the temperature rise directly. An increase in temperature rise from such a device would clearly show when a machine is being overloaded or if the coolant circuits are not performing as they should. But the method is still relatively insensitive to any localised overheating somewhere in the electrically active parts of the machines.

Considerable effort has therefore been devoted, as an alternative to the thermal image, to devising a method whereby a single indication of high temperature is obtained from a device

238

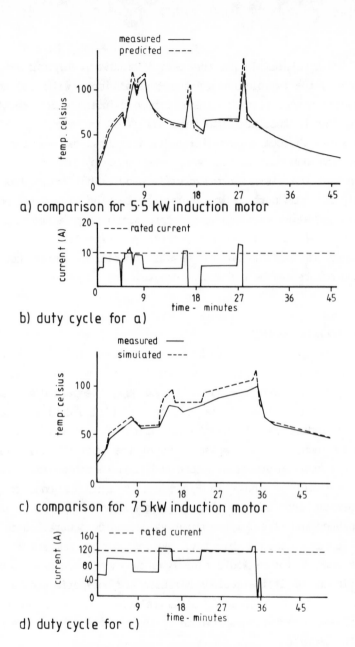

a) comparison for 5·5 kW induction motor

b) duty cycle for a)

c) comparison for 75 kW induction motor

d) duty cycle for c)

Figure 7.5 : Comparison between measurements and the predictions
of a thermal image of an electrical machine
Taken from [7.7]
© IEEE (1986)

which is embedded in the bulk of the machine. Lengths of signal cable using heat-sensitive semi-conducting material as the insulation have been proposed but most effort has been devoted to the use of optical fibres. Gottlieb and Brandt [7.8] have described various methods, including simple point measurements on high voltage components, using the optical fibre for isolation purposes. But they have also described how, using the temperature sensitive properties of fibre optics, a continuously-sensitive fibre could be embedded in the machine, adjacent to the high voltage copper, to detect localised overheating anywhere in the winding and yet provide a single indication. The method proposed would utilise the black body radiation in the optical fibre, alongside the hot spot, being transmitted back to the detector and being used to determine the hottest point along the fibre's length. Such a device would therefore need to be embedded in the machine during manufacture and as yet a practicable instrumentation scheme has not been devised.

7.5 CONCLUSIONS

This Chapter shows that although temperature measurement is usually done in traditional and rather antiquated ways, there are some simple changes that could be made in existing practice to make more sense of temperature measurement. But these changes are generally in the area of signal processing. There are also a number of new temperature monitoring techniques becoming available, which will allow temperature measurements to get closer to the active parts of a machine, and these should be exploited.

CHAPTER 8

The Application of Monitoring — Case Studies

8.1   GENERAL

This chapter shows how the techniques described in earlier chapters are applied practically to electrical machines. In the first section we consider the application of a number of techniques to one machine, in what we have called multiparameter monitoring. The later sections deal with particular case studies, first on generators and then on motors.

8.2   MULTIPARAMETER MONITORING

8.2.1   General

In practice relatively few of the techniques described in previous chapters are applied to all machines. For example Figures 8.1 and 8.2 show the standard monitoring methods applied to a large generator and a large motor at this time in the U.K. There are benefits in applying more monitoring techniques but the benefits depend upon the machine concerned and, in particular, upon the particular faults which a machine is likely to experience. This is the most difficult part in determining what monitoring is required, since one cannot foresee the type of operational experience a machine will have. Yet it would be

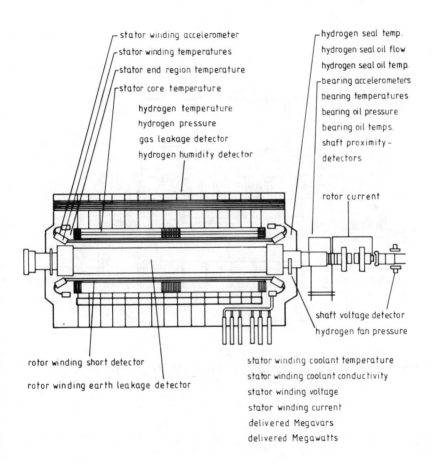

stator winding accelerometer
stator winding temperatures
stator end region temperature
stator core temperature
hydrogen temperature
hydrogen pressure
gas leakage detector
hydrogen humidity detector

hydrogen seal temp.
hydrogen seal oil flow
hydrogen seal oil temp.
bearing accelerometers
bearing temperatures
bearing oil pressure
bearing oil temps.
shaft proximity -
detectors

rotor current

shaft voltage detector
hydrogen fan pressure

rotor winding short detector

rotor winding earth leakage detector

stator winding coolant temperature
stator winding coolant conductivity
stator winding voltage
stator winding current
delivered Megavars
delivered Megawatts

Figure 8.1 : Typical monitoring equipment fitted to a turbogenerator in service in the U.K.

impracticable, except on the largest installation, to fit the widest range of equipment. However, as the earlier chapters will have shown, a number of techniques such as vibration, flux, and current monitoring have a universality which enables them to cover a wide range of defects.

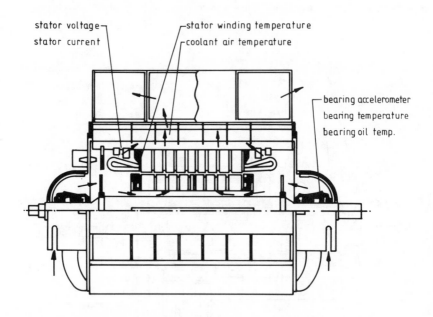

Figure 8.2 : Typical monitoring equipment fitted to a large motor

8.2.2 Generators

Despite these comments, in our experience of applying the techniques described to large turbogenerators we have found that, because of the size and importance of generator plant, no single monitoring signal will be relied upon by operators to give an unequivocal indication of an incipient generator fault.   To provide reliable and convincing warning of damage it is essential to combine a number of indications together in a monitoring system and to interpret between these indications as shown in Figure 8.3. Generator monitoring systems used in the U.K. have been described by Hodge et al. [8.1] and the recommended monitoring to be fitted to a generator is set out in Table 8.1.

A typical multiparameter system for a generator consists of instrumentation for each monitoring technique, usually fitted locally to the machine, cabled back to a data collection system. This is essentially a computer- controlled logger where multiplexing, analogue-to-digital conversion, storage and some limited form of display take place. It is best if such a computer system is small, easy to program and can be fitted close to the machine. However, this sort of processing alone is quite inadequate to form a comprehensive generator monitoring scheme. There must be interpretation between the monitoring indications and much better displays than are possible on a small computer doing the data logging. So Figure 8.3 shows a second block of processing which incorporates software for diagnostic interpretation, alarm indication and display to operators. For a system which is local to a machine it is envisaged that the computer doing this processing could be integrated with the logging processor. But for a large power station with a number of generators the computer could be in the main control room and may even be integrated into the main data processing computer for the plant.

Experience with integrated monitoring on generators in the U.K. has shown the following weaknesses:-

(i) The reliability of monitoring instrumentation has to be very high to meet the needs of continuous monitoring

244

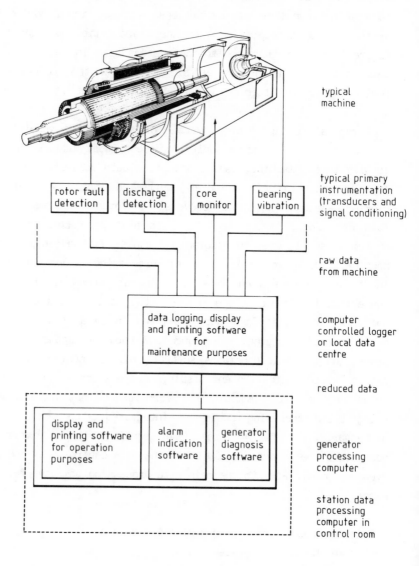

Figure 8.3 : Comprehensive monitoring scheme for a typical
large electrical machine
Taken from [8.2]

TABLE 8.1   RECOMMENDATIONS FOR ON-LINE MONITORING OF GENERATORS

Monitoring Signal	< 250 MW	> 250 MW
STATOR WINDING		
Embedded temperature detectors (ETD) in slot	Yes	Yes
Accelerometers on end winding	No	Yes
STATOR CORE AND FRAME		
ETD, in core	Yes	Yes
ETD, on core end plates	No	Yes
Liquid in frame detector	No	Yes
Accelerometers	No	Yes
Strain gauges	No	Yes
GAS COOLING CIRCUIT		
Gas inlet temperature	Yes	Yes
Gas outlet temperature	Yes	Yes
Gas pressure	Yes	Yes
Fan differential pressure	No	Yes
Humidity detector	No	Yes
Core monitor	No	Yes
WINDING WATER COOLING CIRCUIT		
Water inlet temperature	Yes	Yes
Water outlet temperature	Yes	Yes
Individual conductor outlet temperatures	No	Yes
Water pressure at pumps	No	Yes
Water flow rate	No	Yes
Conductivity meter	Yes	Yes
Gas into water leakage detector	Yes	Yes
Differential pressure across strainers	No	Yes
ROTOR AND SHAFT		
Winding temperature	Yes	Yes
Airgap search coil	No	Yes
Rotor earth detection	No	Yes
Shaft voltage detector	No	Yes
Shaft proximity probes	No	Yes
Phase reference probe	No	Yes
Shaft speed indicator	No	Yes
Shaft torsional monitoring	No	Yes
BEARINGS AND SEALS		
Bearing temperatures	Yes	Yes
Seal temperatures	Yes	Yes
Lub-oil pressure	Yes	Yes
Seal oil pressure	Yes	Yes
Seal oil drain flow rate	No	Yes
Gas in seal oil detection	No	Yes
Accelerometers	Yes	Yes
EXCITATION SYSTEM		
ETDs in stator winding	No	Yes
Air inlet temperature	Yes	Yes
Air outlet temperature	Yes	Yes
Fuse and diode failure detection	No	Yes
TERMINAL QUANTITIES		
Stator voltage	Yes	Yes
Stator current	Yes	Yes
Active power	Yes	Yes
Reactive power	Yes	Yes
COMPREHENSIVE TECHNIQUES		
Gas analysis	No	Yes
Partial discharge analysis	No	Yes
Bearing oil debris analysis	No	Yes
Torsional vibration analysis	No	Yes
Pedestal vibration analysis	Yes	Yes
DISPLAY OF INDICATION		
Alarms only	Yes	Yes
Meter readings	on some signals	on most signals
Mimic diagram	Yes	Yes
Interpretive diagnosis	No	Yes

and this is not always achieved.

(ii) There is an overstatement of the capability of some of the newer monitoring techniques.

(iii) There can be unreliability of the data logging hardware and difficulties with the development of acceptable interpretive software.

(iv) There is often a lack of a sufficiently comprehensive set of monitoring signals on particular generators.

These weaknesses need to be ironed out before an integrated scheme will work effectively.

More recently in the U.S.A., Scherer et al.[8.3] and Gonzales et al.[8.4] have suggested the application of artificial intelligence (AI) techniques to the interpretation and diagnosis of faults on large generators in such an integrated surveillance scheme.

8.2.3 Motors

The recommended monitoring to be fitted to a large motor is summarised in Table 8.2. Our experience shows that with motors the type of integrated schemes using large numbers of inputs, described in 8.2.2, are inappropriate, because the application of only one or two comprehensive monitoring techniques is usually sufficient to provide warning of the majority of faults. However, there may be a good case for applying one or two comprehensive techniques to a large number of motors in a given plant, such as a power station or oil production platform, and carrying out the processing and diagnosis on a central computer.

An example of this approach exists in the monitoring regime that surrounds large induction machines situated on an off-shore oil production platform in the North Sea. On this platform over 150 vibration measurements, together with approximately 30 Shock Pulse Measurements, are recorded on a regular basis from 15 drive trains. The information used here was kindly supplied by Shell U.K. Exploration and Production.

Because of the critical nature of many items of plant on a production platform, the remoteness of the operations, and the very high capitalized losses in the event of an unscheduled outage, a sophisticated monitoring environment is considered to be desirable. To provide this the SPMAP (Shell Platform Machinery Analysis Programme) was instituted in 1984. It provides a good example of the way in which high volumes of information can be data based and analysed as part of the monitoring activity.

The principal method of condition assessment here is via the spectral analysis of vibration velocity signals taken at bearing housings, and Figure 8.4 gives a schematic representation of the system, identifying both the offshore and onshore components.

As the data is collected at each point, the information is coded to identify the measurement point, the load condition of the plant, the collection date, and the instrumentation settings. The home (shore based) system receives the data from the outstation where a range of facilities are available to help an assessment of plant condition to be made. The current record is compared with a baseline spectrum and if the pre-programmed comparison criterion is exceeded then a plot of both spectra is automatically generated and a warning given. The base line can be any designated spectrum or even a synthesis of levels deemed to be appropriate for the particular piece of plant. Information from each record is tagged and stored so that at any time the

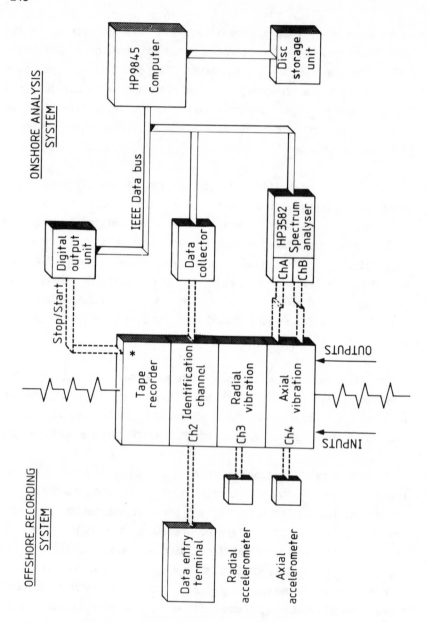

Figure 8.4 : Monitoring and analysis system
(Courtesy of Shell U.K. Expro)

*In an updated version of this system the tape recorder and spectrum analyser have been replaced by a microprocessor based portable data logger.

TABLE 8.2 RECOMMENDATIONS FOR ON-LINE MONITORING OF MOTORS

Item	< 1000 kW	> 1000 kW	High integrity machine
STATOR WINDING			
Embedded temperature detectors (ETDs) in slot position	Yes	Yes	Yes
ETDs in end winding position	No	No	Yes
STATOR FRAME			
Accelerometers	No	No	Yes
MOTOR INTERNAL COOLING CIRCUIT			
Air inlet temperature	Yes	Yes	Yes
Air outlet temperature	Yes	Yes	Yes
MOTOR EXTERNAL COOLING CIRCUIT AIR TO AIR OR WATER			
Air inlet temperature	No	Yes	Yes
Air outlet temperature	No	Yes	Yes
Air flow	No	Yes	Yes
Water inlet temperature	No	Yes	Yes
Water outlet temperature	No	Yes	Yes
Water flow	No	Yes	Yes
BEARINGS			
Shock pulse monitoring	No	Yes	Yes
Bearing oil temperature	No	Yes	Yes
Bearing temperature	Yes	Yes	Yes
Oil level or flow indicator	No	Yes	Yes
Bearing accelerometers	No	Yes	Yes
SHAFT			
Shaft proximity probes	No	No	Yes
Phase reference probe	No	No	Yes
TERMINAL QUANTITIES			
Voltage	Yes	Yes	Yes
Current	Yes	Yes	Yes
Power	No	No	Yes
COMPREHENSIVE TECHNIQUES			
Stator current analysis	No	Yes	
Axial flux analysis	No	No	
Cooling gas analysis	No	No	as required
Partial dischrage analysis	No	No	
Speed fluctuation analysis	No	No	
Bearing oil debris analysis	No	No	
DISPLAY OF INDICATIONS			
Alarms only	Yes	Yes	Yes
Meter readings	No	on some signals	on some signals
Mimic readings	No	No	Yes
Interpretive diagnosis	No	No	Yes

history of a particular measurement point can be recalled, and the data trended. This allows maintenance staff to correlate plant status and repair record with operational performance.

8.3 MONITORING LARGE TURBINE GENERATORS

We have applied many of the techniques described in earlier chapters to a variety of turbine generators and have provided information, which has been useful to power station staff for maintenance purposes, in a particular fault situation. However, only on relatively few machines have we been able to apply sufficient techniques to give the multiparameter capability which we now believe is necessary for continuous monitoring of large generators. The following pages give details our experience with two systems.

At one power station, the 350 MW generators, which are of an old design, were experiencing faults in their stator winding which caused arcing between subconductors leading to perforation of water-cooled subconductors, overheating of the insulation and eventually a phase-to-phase or phase-to-earth fault. Figure 8.5 shows the ultimate outcome of a similar incident. To provide early warning of this activity, rf discharge monitors, core monitors and gas leakage meters were fitted to the generators considered to be most at risk. The monitors were chosen to detect those consequences of the machine fault which were most likely to give the maximum amount of warning of failure: that is discharge activity, burning of insulation and the leakage of hydrogen into the water circuit. This is an example of tailoring the monitoring to suit the particular faults which are expected. The list of signals monitored is tabulated in Table 8.1. The indications were scanned by a logger, in an arrangement shown in Figure 8.6. Data was displayed on a VDU, printed out on paper and stored on a floppy disc, although the latter proved too

Figure 8.5 : Example of damage to a generator after
a stator winding fault
Taken from [8.2]

unreliable for long term analysis. The system was not incorporated into control room displays because the faults developed
slowly over many weeks and it was found adequate to make routine
inspections of the logger indications. A photograph of the
system is shown in Figure 8.7. The results of this exercise were
reported by Miller et al.[8.5] and show that on two separate
machines the development of subconductor arcing faults could be
traced over a number of weeks. When this occurred the machines
were removed from service for repair at a time which coincided
with other repair work, enabling the overall outage time to be
minimised. So the system provided additional information to the
power station staff to help them in their decision about the
scheduling of repair work. The system did not provide on-line
operational information, nor did it have any interpret or
diagnostic capability in its software.

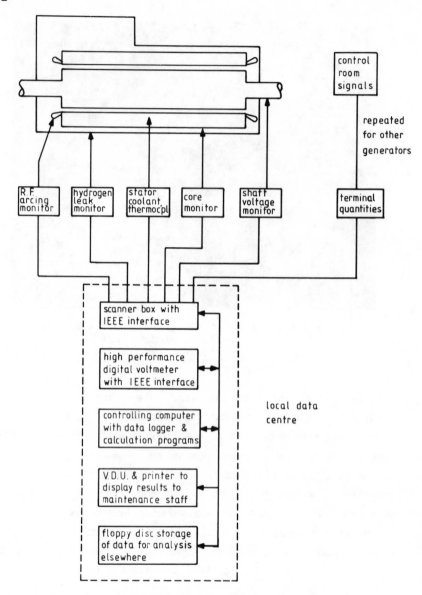

Figure 8.6 : Example of a monitoring system on a
number of 350 MW generators

Figure 8.7 : Photograph of a monitoring system on a
number of 350 MW generators
(Courtesy of CEGB)

At another power station a more advanced monitoring system has
been installed on two 500 MW generators which originally had
similar subconductor arcing problems but where, because of the
winding design, the fault developed much more rapidly. The
system incorporates features to take account of some of the
lessons learnt in the earlier exercise. First a reliable
proprietary data-logger with its own computer was used; this
allowed simple, fault-free programming and enabled both processing and interpretive tasks to be undertaken. Secondly, a
simple graphical output of important monitored quantities was
provided and the data stored on more reliable cassettes so that

they could be analysed in more detail when problems arose. Thirdly, simple alarm information was presented to the power station operating staff so that prompt action could be taken when a fault developed. The system is shown schematically in Figure 8.8. In this case the system operated satisfactorily and detected a major subconductor arcing fault before it had progressed to a phase-to-earth or phase-to-phase fault, although the warning it gave was very short. When the subconductor arcing fault had been repaired and the generator put back into service the monitoring system gave confidence that no further deterioration was taking place. The list of signals monitored by this scheme is also given in Table 8.3. More modern large generators in the U.K. do not incorporate stator winding designs which suffer from this type of subconductor arcing, but monitoring systems can still be of benefit in providing early warning of incipient defects.

In the U.S. the generator monitoring scheme which incorporates AI, as described by Gonzales et al.[8.4], has been applied to a number of turbine generator plants at different locations, as shown in Figure 8.9. The list of signals monitored on each set is given in Table 8.3 and it can be seen that the coverage is more extensive than in the two U.K. examples. In this case monitoring data is communicated automatically from a Data Centre or logging unit local to the plant, to a central diagnostic centre where the diagnosis, alarms and display activities of Figure 8.3 are concentrated in one large computer in which artificial intelligence techniques can be applied. The authors give the following advantages for such an arrangement: it lets the knowledge engineer and experts monitor the accuracy of the diagnosis and make base modifications when necessary; it allows the experts to identify problems and solutions common to several plants. Local plants do not then require the sophisticated computer installations necessary to run AI software. Also improvements in the diagnostic program do not require repro-

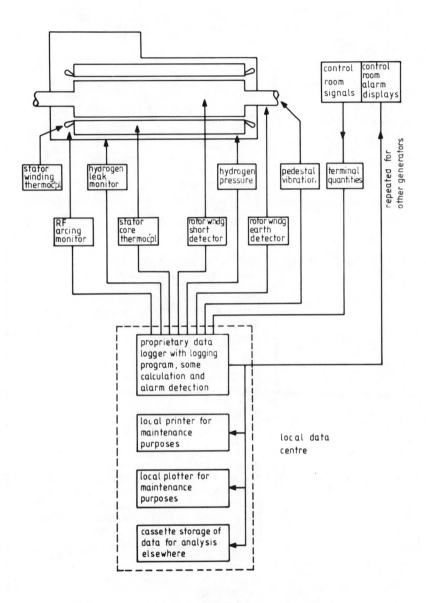

Figure 8.8 : Example of a monitoring system on
a number of 500 MW generators

TABLE 8.3   SIGNALS INCORPORATED INTO GENERATOR
MONITORING SCHEMES

Generator Monitoring System	Signals Incorporated
UK 350 MW Generator Scheme	Core monitor Hydrogen leakage detector Shaft voltage Stator winding thermocouples MW delivered Stator current Stator voltage Core monitor RF arcing monitor
UK 500 MW Generator Scheme	Hydrogen leakage detector Stator winding thermocouples Stator core thermocouples Rotor winding short circuit detector Rotor winding earth leakage detector Generator pedestal vibration amplitudes Hydrogen pressure MW delivered MVAr delivered Stator current Stator voltage Core monitor RF arcing monitor
US Generator Scheme	Hydrogen leakage detector Stator winding thermocouple Stator winding water circuit pressure Stator winding water flow rate Stator core thermocouple Rotor winding earth leakage detector Hydrogen pressure detector Hydrogen humidity meter Turbine generator pedestal vibration amplitudes Torsional vibration MW delivered MVAr delivered Stator current Stator voltage

gramming of every Data Centre in the field. On the other hand this approach is only applicable for one turbine-generator manufacturer or where a large number of plants are owned by one company.

In these generator case studies, the experience has shown the overriding need for ensuring the highest possible reliability of both the primary monitoring instrumentation and the logging system. This is particularly important if the output from the system is to be used by operating staff and false alarms avoided. Considerable experience needs to be built up using such systems before they will be widely believed and relied upon, so that when an alarm is given it is acted upon.

8.4 MONITORING LARGE MOTORS

We can now look at two case studies in which incipient faults on motors were identified using the SPMAP system described in Section 8.2.3 and how monitoring is done on high integrity drives in a nuclear power station.

8.4.1 Out of Balance Vibration

This study refers to a sea water injection pump set, comprising the pump driven by a 6.6 kV, 3.6 MW, 3560 rpm cage induction machine.

At the start of the programme of monitoring it was perceived that the overall radial vibration level, measured at the motor bearings, was too high and that the principal component was at the fundamental rotational frequency. This was diagnosed as rotor unbalance, and the machine was subsequently rebalanced.

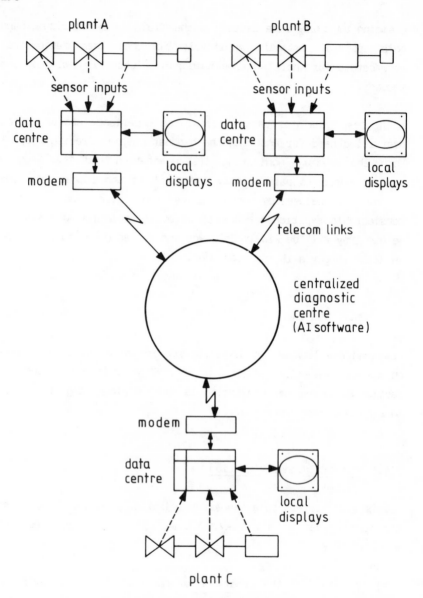

Figure 8.9 : Centralised on-line diagnostic system to
turbine generators
Taken from [8.4]
© IEEE (1985)

Figure 8.10 shows the records produced by the monitoring system before and after balancing. It can be seen that the overall vibration level has fallen from 10.5 mm s^{-1} to 4.7 mm s^{-1}, whilst the level of the fundamental component has reduced to 4.1 mm s^{-1}, from 10.0 mm s^{-1}.

8.4.2 Identification of Cracked Rotor Bars

This study indicated the presence of loose bars in the rotor of a gas booster compressor drive. The machine is a 2-pole 6.6 kV cage induction machine with a nominal speed of 3570 rpm.

The vibration spectra from this machine indicated a degree of electromagnetically induced components, principally the twice line frequency peak at 120 Hz, and the higher frequencies at 5, 6, 7 and 8 times the running speed. Although the overall level of vibration was still relatively low, the characteristics of the spectra held the key to the diagnosis of broken bars. A shut down and subsequent inspection of the rotor revealed several faulty bars, and it was considered likely that, if the machine had been allowed to continue operating in this condition, then a catastrophic failure due to rotor/stator contact would have resulted.

The spectral changes at 2 monthly intervals are illustrated in Figure 8.11, and for comparison the post-repair spectrum is also shown.

The benefits of this monitoring programme are immediately obvious.

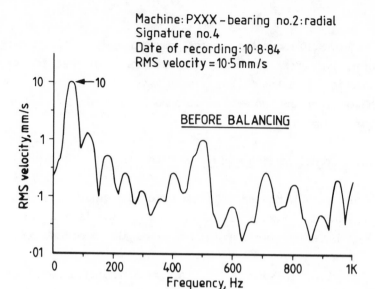

Machine: PXXX – bearing no.2: radial
Signature no.4
Date of recording: 10·8·84
RMS velocity = 10·5 mm/s

BEFORE BALANCING

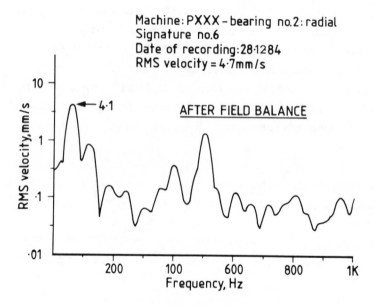

Machine: PXXX – bearing no.2: radial
Signature no.6
Date of recording: 28·12·84
RMS velocity = 4·7mm/s

AFTER FIELD BALANCE

Figure 8.10 : The effect of balancing on bearing vibration
(Courtesy of Shell U.K. Expro)

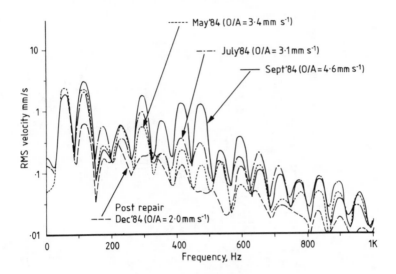

Machine:KXXX-bearing no.1:radial

Figure 8.11 : Progressive degradation due to
rotor-bar looseness
(Courtesy of Shell U.K. Expro)

8.4.3 Monitoring Points on a Typical System

In addition to vibration velocity and SPM level many other of
the parameters we have mentioned in previous chapters would be
routinely monitored. This is illustrated in Figure 8.12 which
gives a line diagram representation of the utilities and
monitoring points surrounding a centrifugal gas compressor and
drive, coupled via a gearbox being monitored by SPMAP.

In this diagram the meaning of the identifiers associated with
each monitoring point is given in Table 8.4.

262

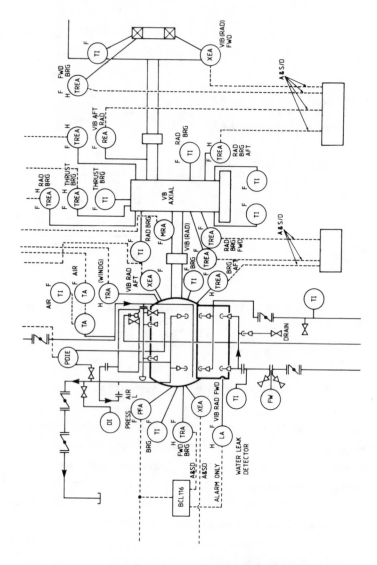

Figure 8.12 : Utilities and monitoring points on a typical gas
compressor on SPMAP

(Courtesy of Shell U.K. Expro)

TABLE 8.4 COMPRESSOR DRIVE MONITORING POINTS

Mnemonic	Signal collected
T1	Temperature
TA	Temperature
TRA	Temperature
TREA	Temperature
XEA	Vibration
LA	Lubrication supply level
PT	Pressure

8.4.4 Monitoring of a High Integrity Drive in a Nuclear Power Station

This case study concerns the monitoring of a 2-pole 5 MW squirrel cage induction motor driving a gas circulator in an advanced gas-cooled reactor (AGR). The motor is nose-suspended and was submerged in carbon dioxide in the reactor at 40 atmospheres; it is described by Schwarz et al.[8.6, 8.7, 8.8]. The gas temperature in the reactor is 300 °C but this is cooled for the motor environment to 60 °C. The motors are expected to run continuously for up to two years without being withdrawn from the reactor for inspection. This motor is being used in an exceptionally arduous environment, in a particularly important application, and with over 40 machines now in service the true service needs have been brought to light.

The major concern during design was the level of vibration that would be experienced by the frame and the windings, bearing in mind that the machines were nose-suspended. It was also important to ensure that the machines were running within their rating. The former monitoring is achieved by frame accelerometers and shaft proximity probes while the latter is achieved by embedded temperature detectors in the slot and end winding portions. Because the machines are inaccessible for long periods there has been a concern to monitor in-service not only the vibration performance but also the integrity of the rotor cage and the stator winding insulation, both of which are highly stressed. So some of the newer techniques described in Chapters 4 and 6 have been used. In particular, stator current analysis and speed analysis for rotor problems and on-line discharge detection for stator winding problems. The monitoring generally follows that listed in column 4 of Table 8.2.

The indications from the monitoring transducers have been connected into the power station computing system where the data can be displayed on a VDU or recorded on a printer. No software diagnosis is made but on more modern stations the data is presented on a mimic diagram and alarm conditions highlighted in red, which can help the operator to diagnose problems himself.

Experience has shown that simple displays in the control room of alarm information from monitoring signals are quite adequate, even for machines of this complexity, and there is no need for the more sophisticated diagnosis between monitoring signals, as has been proposed for turbogenerators.

References

CHAPTER 1

1.1 The Electricity Council: Power System Protection,
Vol. 1, Principles and Components,
Peter Peregrinus, Stevenage. 1981.

1.2 Neale, N. and Associates: A guide to the condition
monitoring of machinery,
HMSO, London, 1979.

1.3 Malin, J.L., Bunton, I.: HP maintenance management: A new
approach to software customer solutions,
Hewlett-Packard Journal, March 1985, pp 4-10.

CHAPTER 2

2.1 Say, M.G. ed.: Electrical Engineers' Reference Book
Newnes-Butterworths, London, 1977, Chap. 4.

2.2 International Electrotechnical Commission Publication 85,
1957.

2.3 British Standard 2757:1956: Classification of insulating
materials for electrical machinery and apparatus on the
basis of thermal stability in service,
British Standards Institution, London.

2.4 Werninck, E.H., ed: Electric Motor Handbook,
McGraw Hill, Maidenhead, 1978, Chap. 5.

2.5 Bone, J.C.H. and Schwarz, K.K.: Large a.c. motors,
Proc. IEE, Vol. 120, No. 10R, October 1973, pp 1111-1132.

2.6 Barker, B. and Hodge, J.M.: A decade of experience with generator and large motor reliability, CIGRE, Paris, 1-9 September 1982, Paper 11-07.

CHAPTER 3

3.1 Allocca, J.A., Stuart, A.: Transducers : Theory and Application, Reston Publishing Co., Reston, 1984.

3.2 Oliver, F.J.: Practical Instrumentation Transducers, Pitman, London, 1972

3.3 Brüel and Kjær: Measuring Vibration, Bruel and Kjær, Naerum, 1980.

3.4 Brüel and Kjær: Machine Health Monitoring, Brüel and Kjær, Naerum, 1984.

3.5 Barney, G.C.: Intelligent Instrumentation, Prentice Hall Int., London, 1985

3.6 Garside, R.: Intrinsically Safe Instrumentation Safety Technology, Feltham, 1982.

3.7 Application Note 243-1: Dynamic signal analyser applications, Hewlett-Packard, Palo Alto, 1983.

3.8 Randall, R.B.: Application of Brüel and Kjær Equipment to Frequency Analysis, Brüel and Kjær, Naerum, 1977.

3.9 Antoniou, A.: Digital Filters : Analysis and Design, McGraw-Hill, New York, 1979.

3.10 de Sa, A.: Principles of Electronic Instrumentation, Edward Arnold, London, 1981.

CHAPTER 4

4.1 Emery, F.T., Lenderking, B.N. Couch, R.D.: Turbine-generator on-line diagnostics using RF monitoring, IEEE Trans. on Power Appl. and Sys., Vol. PAS-100, No. 12, December 1981, pp 4974-4982.

4.2 Harrold, R.T., Emery, F.T., Murphy, F.J., Drinkut, S.A.:
Radio frequency sensing of incipient arcing faults within
large turbine generators,
IEEE Trans. on Power Appl. and Sys., Vol. PAS-98, No. 4,
July/Aug. 1979, pp 1167-1173.

4.3 Timperley, J.E.: Incipient fault detection through neutral
RF monitoring of large rotating machines,
IEEE Trans. on Power Appl. and Sys., Vol. PAS-102, No. 3,
March 1983, pp 693-698.

4.4 Wilson, A., Nye, A.E.T., Hopgood, D.J.: On-line detection
of partial discharges in hv plant,
4th BEAMA International Electrical Insulation Conference,
Brighton, UK, May 1982, pp 233-239.

4.5 Ward, D.A.: Improvements in or relating to alternating
current measurement,
UK Patent Application 444 10/78, 1978.

4.6 Wilson, A. and Stannett, A.W.: Detection of incipient
insulation faults in power equipment using earth loop
transient monitoring,
CEGB Technical Disclosure Bulletin No. 305, May 1977.

4.7 Kurtz, M. and Stone, G.C.: In-service partial discharge
testing of generator insulation,
IEEE Trans. of Electr. Insul., Vol. EI-14, No. 2, April
1979, pp 94-100.

4.8 Kurtz, M., Stone, G.C., Freeman, D., Mulhall, V.R.,
Lonseth, P.: Diagnostic testing of generator insulation
without service interruption
CIGRE, Paris 1980, Paper 11-09.

4.9 Malik, A.K., Cook, R.F. and Tavner, P.J.: The detection of
discharges in alternators using wideband radio frequency
techniques
Proc. of Int. Conf. on Electrical Machines - Design and
Applications, IEE, London, September 1985, Conference Publn.
254, pp 121-125.

4.10 Michiguchi, Y., Tonisaka, S., Izumi, S., Watanabe, T.
Miyashita, I.: Development of a collector ring monitor for
sparking detection on generators,
IEEE Trans. Power Appl. and Sys., Vol. PAS-102, No. 4,
1983, pp 928-933.

4.11 Warrington, A.W. Van C.:   Protective relays, Their Theory and Practice, Vol. 1, Chapman and Hall Ltd., London 1982.

4.12 Hargis, C., Muhlhaus, J., Roberts, I.A. and Sutton, J.: Turbo-generator rotor earth fault monitoring and protection, Proc. of Int. Conf. on Electrical Machines - Design and Applications, IEE, London, Conference Publ. 254, September 1985, pp 6-10.

4.13 Rosenberg, L.T.:   Influence of shorted turns on thermal unbalance in large generators IEEE, PES Summer Meeting, Los Angeles, July 1978, Paper A78, 587-8.

4.14 Khudabashev, K.A.:   Effect of turn short-circuits in a turbo-generator rotor on its state of vibration, Elekt Stantsii (Russian), No. 7, 1961, pp 40-45.

4.15 Albright, D.R.:   Inter-turn short circuit detector for turbine generator rotor windings, IEEE Trans. Power Appl. and Sys. Vol., PAS-50, 1971, pp 478-483.

4.16 Conolly, H.M., Jackson, R.J., Lodge, I. and Roberts, I.A.: Detection of shorted turns in generator rotor windings using air gap search coils, Proc. of Int. Conf. on Electrical Machines - Design and Applications, IEE, London, Conference Publn. 254, September 1985, pp 11-15.

4.17 Byars, M.:   Detection of alternator rotor winding faults using an on-line magnetic field search coil monitoring unit, Proc. of 17th Universities Power Engineering Conference, Manchester, 30th March - 1st April, 1982.

4.18 Kryukhin, S.S.:   A new principle for synchronous machine protection from rotor winding inter-turn and double earth faults, Elect. Technol. USSR, Vol. 2, 1972, pp 47-59.

4.19 Muhlhaus, J., Ward, D.M. and Lodge, I.:   The detection of shorted turns in generator rotor windings by measurement of circulating stator currents, Proc. of Int. Conf. on Electrical Machines - Design and Applications, IEE, London, Conference Publn. 254, September 1985, pp 100-103.

4.20 Buckley, G.W.: The effects of rotor inter-turn short-circuits on voltage imbalance and circulating currents in large generator stator windings,
Proc. of Int. Conf. on Electrical Machines - Design and Applications, IEE, London, Conference Publn. 213, July 1982, pp 206-211.

4.21 Grant, A.E.: Turbo-generator rotor winding fault detection by a recurrent surge method,
CEGB, U.K., Technical Disclosure Bulletin, No. 201, July 1973.

4.22 Barker, B. and Hodge, J.M.: A decade of experience with generator and large motor reliability,
CIGRE, Paris 1982, paper 11-07.

4.23 Kamerbeek, E.M.H.: Torque measurements on induction motors using Hall generators or measuring windings,
Philips Technical Review, Vol. 34, 1974, No. 7, pp 152-162.

4.24 Hargis, C., Gaydon, B.G. and Kamash, K.: The detection of rotor defects in induction motors,
Proc. of Int. Conf. on Electrical Machines - Design and Applications, IEE, London, Conference Publn. 213, July 1982, pp 216-220.

4.25 Jufer, M. and Abdulaziz, M.: Influence d'une rupture de barre ou d'un anneau sur les characteristiques externes d'un moteur asynchrone a cage,
Bull SEV/VSE (Switzerland), Vol. 69, No. 17, September 1978.

4.26 Steele, M.E., Ashen, R.A. and Knight, L.G.: An electrical method of monitoring motors,
Proc. of Int. Conf. on Electrical Machines - Design and Applications, IEE, London, Conference Publn. 213, July 1982, pp 231-235.

4.27 Notelet, F. and Ravalitera G.: Assessment of the induction motor eccentricity deduced from fluctuations of the feeding currents,
Proc. of Int. Conf. on Electrical Machines, Lausanne, Switzerland, 18-21 September 1984, pp 1177-1179.

4.28 Rickson, C.D.: Protecting motors from overload due to asymmetrical fault conditions,
Electrical Review, 7th December 1983, pp 778-780.

4.29 Ellison, D.H., Exon, J.L.T. and Ward, D.A.: Protection of slip ring induction motors,
Proc. of Conf. on Developments in Power System Protection, IEE,
London, Conference Publn. 185, July 1980, pp 49-53.

4.30 Verma, S.P. and Girgis, R.S.: Shaft potentials and currents in large turbogenerators,
Report for the Canadian Electrical Association, No. 78-69, May 1981.

4.31 Jordan, H, Kovacs, K., Roder, P.: Messungen des schlupfes von asynchronmaschinen mit einer spule,
Elektrotech Z, (German), Vol. 86, 1965, pp 294-296.

4.32 Jordan, H. and Taegen F.: Wellenflusse infolge con schwankungen des luftapalteitwertes,
Electrotech Z, (German), Vol. 85, 1964, pp 865-867.

4.33 Erlicki, M.S., Porat, Y, Alexandrovitz, A.: Leakage field changes of an induction motor as indication of non-symmetric supply,
IEEE Trans. Gen. Appl., Vol. IGA-7, No. 6, Nov./Dec. 1971, pp 713-717.

4.34 Penman, J., Hadwick, J.G., Stronach, A.F.: Protection strategy against the occurrence of faults in electrical machines,
Proc. of 2nd Int. Conf. on Developments in Power System Protection IEE, London, Conference Publn. 185, June 1980, pp 54-58.

4.35 Penman, J., Tait, A.J., Smith, J.R. and Bryan, W.E.: The development of a machine condition monitoring system for electrical drives,
Proc. of Conf. on Drives, Motors and Controls, 1985.

4.36 Seinsch, H.O.: Detection and diagnosis of abnormal operating conditions and/or faults in rotating electrical machines,
Scharch Berichte, Ausgabe 1986.

CHAPTER 5

5.1 Skala, G.F.: The ion chamber detector as a monitor of thermally produced particulates,
J. de Res. Atmos, 1966, April/Sept.

5.2 Carson, C.C., Barton, S.C. and Grobel, L.P.:   Immediate
     detection of overheating in gas-cooled electrical
     machines,
     IEEE PES Winter Power Meeting, January 1971, Paper 71CP,
     154-PWR.

5.3 Carson, C.C., Barton, S.C. and Echeverria, F.S.: Immediate
     warning of local overheating in electrical machines by the
     detection of pyrolysis products,
     IEEE Trans. Pow. Appl. & Sys., Vol. PAS-92, January/June
     1973, pp 533-542.

5.4 Wood, J.W., Ryan, M.J., Gallagher, P. and Gunton, D.:
     Condition monitoring of turbogenerators,
     Proc. Int. Conf. of Electrical Machines - Design and
     Applications, IEE, London, 13-15 July 1982, Conference
     Publn. 213, pp 131-135.

5.5 Lodge, I.:   Prevention of catastrophic failure of large
     generators by early detection of overheating,
     Proc. Int. Conf. of Electrical Machines - Design and
     Applications, IEE, London, Conference Publn. 213, pp
     123-130.

5.6 Carson, C.C., Barton, S.C. and Gill, R.S.: The occurrence
     and control of interference from oil-mist in the detection
     of overheating in a generator,
     IEE Trans. Pow. App. & Sys., Vol. PAS-57, No. 5, Sept/Oct
     1978, pp 1590-1514.

5.7 Ryder, D.M., Wood, J.W. and Gallagher, P.L.:   The
     detection and identification of overheated insulation in
     turbo-generators,
     IEEE Trans. Pow. Appl. and Sys., Vol. PAS-98, No. 7, Jan/
     Feb. 1979, pp 333-336.

5.8 Hogg, W.K. and Ryder, D.M.:   The influence of particle
     size emitted thermally from insulation, coding compounds
     and contamination on condition monitor responses,
     Proc. of Int. Conf. on Electrical Machines-Design and
     Applications, IEE, London, Sept. 1985, Publn. 254, pp 118-
     120.

5.9 Dear, D.J.A., Dillon, A.F. and Freedman, A.N.:
     Determination of organic compounds in the hydrogen used
     for cooling large electricity generators,
     Journal of Chromatograpy, Vol. 137, 1977, pp 315-322.

5.10 Kelley, J.K., Auld, J.W., Herter, V.J., Hutchinson, K.A. and Rugenstein, W.A.: Early detection and diagnosis of overheating problems in turbine generators by instrumental chemical analysis, IEEE Trans. Pow. Appl. & Sys., Vol. PAS-95, No. 3, May/June 1976, pp 879-886.

5.11 Goodman, D.M.: Gas analysis techniques to monitor generator insulation. Colloquium on insulation condition monitoring in generators, IEE, London 21st May 1982, Colloquium Digest No. 1982/57.

5.12 Le Gall, Y. and Pasdeloup, M.: Detection des echauffements dans les turbo-alternateurs refroidis a l'hydrogene, Rev. Gen. Elect., (French), Vol. 87, No. 12, December 1978, pp 963-968.

5.13 Painter, M.R., Bratt, E.C. and Painton, R.F.: Assessment of the benefits of generator insulation fault detection by hydrogen analysis, U.K. CEGB Internal Report, January 1982.

5.14 Burton, P.J. and Gaydon, B.G.: An on-line gas monitoring system for fault detection in totally enclosed air-cooled motors, Proc. of 21st Universities Power Engineering Conf., Imperial College, London, 15-17 April 1986.

5.15 Evans, C.: Wear debris analysis and condition monitoring, NDT International, Vol. 11, No. 3, 1978, pp 132-134.

5.16 Bowen, R., Scott, D., Siefert, W. and Westcott, V.C.: Ferrography Tribology International, Vol. 9, No. 3, June 1976, pp 109-115.

5.17 Verma, S.P. and Girgis, R.S.: Shaft potentials and currents in large turbogenerators, Report for the Canadian Electrical Association No. 78-69, May 1981.

5.18 Rogers, R.: Concepts used in the development of the IEEE and IEC codes for the interpretation of incipient faults in power transformers by dissolved gas in oil analysis, IEEE PES, Winter Power Meeting, New York, January 1978.

5.19 Neale, N. and Associates: A guide to the condition monitoring of machinery, HMSO, London, 1979.

5.20 Metal particle detector systems,
     Smiths Industries, Aviation Division, Publication No.
     SAV 380T.

5.21 Lloyd, O. and Hammond, W.A.: (inventors) Improvements in
     or relating to the collection and sensing of magnetic
     debris in lubricating oil and other liquids,
     U.K. Patent GB2, 029, 580B.

5.22 Bogue, R.W.: An improved magnetic plug for the continuous
     monitoring of wear debris,
     Proc. Int. Conf. on Condition Monitoring, Swansea, April
     1984, pp 628-636.

5.23 Lloyd, O. and Cox, A.F.: Monitoring debris in turbine
     generator oil,
     Wear, Vol. 71, 1981, pp 79-91.

5.24 Lloyd, O., Cox, A.F. and Hammond, W.A.: An automatic on-
     line debris in oil monitor and sampler,
     Proc. Int. Conf. on Condition Monitoring, Brighton, 21-23
     May, 1986.

5.25 Cox, A.F., Glanville, R., Lloyd, O. and Robins, U.K.
     (inventors): Apparatus for monitoring particulate matter,
     U.K. Patent Application GB2, 138, 565A.

CHAPTER 6

6.1 Alger, P.L.: Induction Machines,
    John Wiley and Sons, New York, 1951.

6.2 Jordan, H.: The Low Noise Electric Motor,
    Essen, Germany, 1950.

6.3 Erdelyi, E., Erie, P.A., Haway, G.: Vibration modes of
    states of induction motors,
    Trans. ASME, Paper A-28, 1956, pp 39-45.

6.4 Yang, S.: Low Noise Electric Motors,
    IEE Monograph, Clarendon Press, Oxford, 1981.

6.5 Timoshenko, S.: Vibration Problems in Engineering,
    Van Nostrand Inc., New York, 1947.

6.6 Jordan, H., Frohne, H.: Emittlung der Eigenfrequenzen de
    Stander van Archstranmaten,
    Lambekampfung, No. 7, pp 137-40.

274

6.7 Penman, J., Chalmers, B.J., Kamar, A., Tuncay, N.: The performance of solid steel secondary linear induction machines,
Trans. IEEE (PAS), Vol. PAS-100, No. 6, 1981, pp 2927-2935.

6.8 Williamson, S., Laithwaite, E.: Generalised harmonic analysis,
Proc. IEE, Pt. B, Vol. 132, No. 3, 1985, pp 157-163.

6.9 Hague, B.: Principles Of Electromagnetism Applied To Electrical Machines,
Dover, New York, 1962.

6.10 Stafl, M.: Electrodynamics Of Electrical Machines,
Academia, Prague, 1967.

6.11 Binns, K.J., Dye, M.: Identification of principal factors affecting unbalanced magnetic pull in cage induction motors,
Proc. IEE, Vol. 120, March 1973, pp 349-354.

6.12 Swann, S.A.: Effect of rotor eccentricity on the magnetic field of a non-salient pole machine,
Proc. IEE, Vol. 110, 1963, pp 903-915.

6.13 Rai, R.B.: Airgap eccentricity in induction motors,
ERA Report, 1974, pp 1174-1188.

6.14 Binns, K.J.: Cogging torques in induction machines,
Proc. IEE, Vol. 115, 1968, pp 1783-1790.

6.15 Lim, C.Y.: Characteristics of reluctance motors,
IEEE Trans. Pow. App. & Sys., Vol. PAS-70, Pt. II, 1951, pp 1971-1978.

6.16 Carpenter, C.J.: Surface integral methods of calculating force on magnetized iron parts,
IEE Monograph No. 342, 1959.

6.17 Brandl, P.: Forces on the end windings of a.c. machines,
Brown Boveri Review, Vol. 2, 1980, pp 128-134.

6.18 Ontaguro, M. Yagiuchi, K. and Yamaguchi, H.: Mechanical behaviour of stator endwindings,
IEEE Trans. (PAS), Vol. PAS-99, No. 3, May/June 1980, pp 1181-1185.

6.19 Campbell, J.J., Clark, P.E., McShane, I.E. Wakeley, K.:
      Strains on motor endwindings.
      IEEE Trans. (IAS), Vol. IA-20, NO. 1, January/February
      1984, pp 37-44.

6.20 Wort, J.F.G.: The fundamentals of industrial balancing
      machines and their applications,
      Brüel and Kjær Review No. 1, 1981, pp 3-31.

6.21 Dimentberg, F.M.: Flexural vibrations of rotating shafts,
      Butterworths, London, 1961.

6.22 Walker, D.N., Adams, S.L., Placek, P.J.: Torsional vibra-
      tion and fatigue of turbine generator shafts,
      IEEE Trans. (PAS), Vol. PAS-100, No. 11, 1981,
      pp 4373-4080.

6.23 Joyce, J.S., Lambrecht, D.: Status of evaluating the
      fatigue of large steam turbine generation caused by
      electrical disturbances,
      IEEE Trans. (PAS), Vol. PAS-99, No. 1, 1980, pp 111-119.

6.24 Hammons, T.J.: Electrical damping and its effect on
      accumulative life expenditure of turbine generator shafts
      following worst case supply system disturbances,
      IEEE Trans. (PAS), Vol. PAS-102, No. 6, 1983, pp 1552-
      1565.

6.25 Cudworth, C.J., Smith, J.R., Mykura, J.F.: Mechanical
      damping of torsional vibrations in turbogenerators due to
      network disturbances,
      JIME, 1984, pp 139-145.

6.26 Collacott, R.A.: Vibration Monitoring and Diagnostics,
      George Godwin Ltd., London, 1979.

6.27 Ehrich, E.F.: Identification and avoidance of instabil-
      ities and self excited vibrations in rotating machinery,
      ASME Paper No. 72-DE-21.

6.28 Brüel and Kjær: Machine Health Monitoring
      Brüel and Kjær, Naerum, 1984.

6.29 Neale, M. and Associates: A Guide to the Condition
      Monitoring of Machinery,
      HMSO Publication, 1979.

6.30 Mayes, I.W., Steer, A.G. and Thomas, G.B.: The application of vibration monitoring for fault diagnosis in large turbo-generators,
6th Thermal Generation Specialists Meeting, Madrid, 5-6 May 1981.

6.31 Herbert, R.G.: Computer techniques applied to the routine analysis of rundown vibration data for condition monitoring of turbine-alternators,
Proc. Int. Conf. on Condition Monitoring, University College, Swansea, 10-13 April 1984, pp 229-242.

6.32 Erskine, J.B.: A user's view of noise and vibration aspects of a.c. induction motors,
IEE Colloquium on Design Applications and Maintenance of Large Industrial Drives, 1978.

6.33 Leonard, R.A., Thompson, W.T.: Vibration and stray flux monitoring for unbalanced supply and interturn winding fault diagnosis in induction motors,
Proc. 1st U.K. International Conf. on Condition Monitoring Swansea, 1984, pp 340-354.

6.34 Cameron, J.R., Thompson, W.T., Dow, A.B.: Vibration and current monitoring for detecting airgap eccentricity in large induction motors,
Proc. Int. Conf. on Electrical Machines, Design and Applications, IEE, London, September 1985, Publn. 254, pp 173-179.

6.35 Maxwell, J.H.: Induction motor magnetic vibration,
Proc. Vibration Institute, Machinery Vibration Monitoring and Analysis Meeting, Houston, Texas, 1983.

6.36 Hargis, C, Gaydon, B.G., Kamash, K.: The detection of rotor defects in induction motors,
Proc. Int. Conf. on Electrical Machines, Design and Applications, IEE, London, May 1982, Publn. 213.

6.37 Application Note 243-1: Dynamic signal analyser applications,
Hewlett Packard, Palo Alto, 1983.

6.38 Brüel and Kjær: Measuring Vibration
Brüel and Kjær, Naerum, 1980.

6.39 Rusche, P.A.E.: Torsional monitoring for diagnosis and surveillance : utility experience,
EPRI Workshop, USA, 1985, pp 52-66.

6.40 Home, B.P., Walker, D.N.:   Torsional vibration monitoring,
      EPRI Workshop, USA, pp 11-23.

6.41 Gaydon, B.G., Hopgood, D.J.:   Faltering pulse can reveal
      an ailing motor,
      Electrical Review, Vol. 205, No. 14, October 1979,
      pp 37-38.

6.42 Gaydon, B.G.:   An instrument to detect induction motor
      rotor circuit defects by speed fluctuation measurements,
      Testmex Conference, IEE Wembley, June 1979, Conference
      Publn. 174, pp 5-8.

6.43 Schoel, E.O.:   Shock pulses as a measure of the lubricant
      film thickness in roller element bearings,
      Condition Monitoring '84, Ed. M.H. Jones, Pub. Pineridge
      Press, Swansea, 1984, pp 148-161.

6.44 Randall, R.B.:   Cepstrum analysis and gearbox fault diag-
      nosis,
      Brüel and Kjær Publications, Application Note 233, 1980.

CHAPTER 7

7.1   Say, M.G.:   Alternating Current Machines,
      Pitman Publishing, London, 1976, p 137.

7.2   Hampton, B.F. and Medhurst, D.R.:   The Vapotherm method of
      measuring directly the temperature of an EHV transformer
      winding,
      CEGB Technical Disclosure 266, 1976.

7.3   Rogers, A.J.:   Optical temperature sensor for high voltage
      applications,
      Applied Optics, Vol. 21, No. 5, March 1982, pp 882-885.

7.4   Geszti, P.:   Test system for measuring rotor temperature
      using contactless signal transmission,
      Conf. on Evolution and Modern Aspects of Induction
      Machines, Turin, Italy, July 8-11, 1986.

7.5   Siyambalapitiya, D.J.T., McLaren, P.G. and Acarnley, P.P.:
      A rotor condition monitor for squirrel cage induction
      machines,
      IEEE Industrial Applications Society Annual Meeting,
      Denver, U.S.A., Sept. 1986.

7.6 Ramsden, D. and Dring, E.: Thermal protection of small and medium size low tension induction motors, LSE Engineering Bulletin, Vol. 9, No. 2, October 1966, pp 1-20.

7.7 Mellor, P.H., Turner, D.R. and Roberts, D.: Microprocessor based induction motor thermal protection, Proc. Int. Conf. Electrical Machines, Design and Applications, IEE, London, 1985, Publn. 254.

7.8 Gottlieb, M. and Brandt, G.B.: Hot-spot detection in generators with optical fibres, ASME/IEEE Joint Power Generation Conference, October 1981, Missouri, U.S.A., Paper 81-JPGC-PWR-18.

CHAPTER 8

8.1 Hodge, J.M., Miller, T., Roberts, A. and Steel, J.G.: Generator monitoring systems in the United Kingdom, CIGRE, Paris, France, 1-9 September, 1982, Paper 11-08.

8.2 Tavner, P.J., Gaydon, B.G. and Ward, D.M.: Monitoring generators and large motors, Proc. IEE, Vol. 133, Pt. B, No. 3, May 1986, pp 169-180.

8.3 Scherer, H.N., Hajny, M.R., Provananza, J.H., White, T.E.: Monitoring of large generators on the American Electric Power System, CIGRE, Paris, France, 1-9 September 1982, Paper 11-01.

8.4 Gonzales, A.J., Osborne, R.S., Kemper, C.T., Laverfeld, S.: On-line diagnosis of turbine generators using artificial intelligence, IEEE-PES Winter Meeting, New York, U.S.A., February 1985, Paper 85 WM 105/2.

8.5 Miller, T. and Malik, A.K.: Monitoring techniques to improve the availability of 350 MW and 500 MW alternators, IEE Colloquium Digest 1981/25.

8.6 Schwarz, K.K.: Submerged gas-circulator motors for advanced gas-cooled reactors, Proc. IEE, Vol. 120, No. 7, July 1973, pp 777-785.

8.7 Jackson, B., Pestle, J.P. and Wood, M.D.: Recent advances in the design of circulator motors for AGR reactors, IEE Conf. Publ. 254, 1982, pp 18-22.

8.8 Schwarz, K.K.: Three generations of submerged circulator motors for AGR power stations, Proc. IEE, Vol. 132-A, 1983, pp 234-236.

Subject Index

Author Index